Stationary Steam Engines of Great Britain
The National Photographic Collection
Volume 2: Scotland, Cumberland, Co Durham, & Northumberland

George Watkins

The Watkins' Collection in the National Monuments Record

This comprises the photographs and notes George Watkins made during a lifetime of study of the stationary steam engine.

The Steam Engine Record is an annotated set of around 1500 mounted prints of steam engines which Watkins examined in the field between 1930 and 1980. His notebooks contain a record of additional sites for which no photographs were taken, or which comprise written historical notes.
In all almost 2000 entries were made in his notebooks.
There are also albums of prints arranged by engine type. A catalogue is available.

In addition there are files of notes and other records on all aspects of historical steam technology, the cataloguing of which is in progress.

The main areas of this part of the collection are:

Records of steam engine makers.

Collection of bound trade literature.

Classified collection of data files dealing with, for example, textile mill engines, marine engines.

The collection can be inspected by appointment.
Copies of photographs and other documents are readily available.

Please contact:

NMR Enquiry & Research Services
National Monuments Record Centre
Kemble Drive
Swindon
Wilts
SN2 2GZ

STATIONARY STEAM ENGINES OF GREAT BRITAIN

THE NATIONAL PHOTOGRAPHIC COLLECTION

VOLUME 2: SCOTLAND, CUMBERLAND, Co DURHAM & NORTHUMBERLAND

George Watkins

Landmark Publishing

Published by
Landmark Publishing Ltd,
Waterloo House, 12 Compton, Ashbourne, Derbyshire DE6 1DA England
Tel: (01335) 347349 Fax: (01335) 347303
e-mail: landmark@clara.net
web site: www.landmarkpublishing.co.uk

ISBN 1 901 522 06 7

© George Watkins

Print: MPG Ltd, Bodmin, Cornwall
Designed by: James Allsopp
Editor: A P Woolrich
Production: C L M Porter

Front cover: Carr's Flour Mill, Silloth
Back cover: Mauchline Colliery, Mauchline
Page 3: Whitburn Colliery, Whitburn, Sunderland

CONTENTS

29 New Craighall, Newcraighall Colliery, No 3 shaft	SER 1293	56
30 Newtongrange, Lady Victoria Colliery	SER 1290	56
31 Newtongrange, Lingerwood Colliery	SER 1291	60
32 Roslin, Roslin Colliery	SER 1292a	60
33 Roslin, Roslin Colliery	SER 1292b	60

Perthshire

64

34 Blairgowrie, Thompson & Co., Keithbank Works	SER 1262a	64
35 Blairgowrie, Thompson & Co., Keithbank Works	SER 1262b	64
36 Blairgowrie, Thompson & Co., Ashgrove Works	SER 1263a	64
37 Blairgowrie, Thompson & Co., Ashgrove Works	SER 1263b	68
38 Dunblane, Wilson & Sons, woollen mills	SER 1259	68
39 Perth, Perth Waterworks Co., Tay Street Pumping Station	SER 1268	68

Roxburghshire

72

40 Hawick, W. Watson & Sons, Dangerfield Mills	SER 1046	72
41 Jedburgh, Laidlaw's, Allars blanket mills	SER 1048	72

Selkirkshire

72

42 Galashiels, Kemp, Blair & Co., Textile Finishers	SER 1275	72
43 Selkirk, George Roberts & Co., Philiphaugh Mill	SER 1019	76

Stirlingshire

76

44 Alva, Glentana Mills	SER 1258	76

Cumberland

76

45 Cockermouth, Jennings & Co., The Castle Brewery	SER 1443	76
46 Garside, nr Carlisle, The Mental Asylum	SER 612	80
47 Millom, Hodbarrow Iron Ore Mines	SER 554a	80
48 Silloth, Carr's Flour Mill	SER 1249	80
49 Whitehaven, Haig Colliery, No 4 shaft	SER 1444	84
50 Workington, Workington Iron & Steel Co.	SER 1247	84
51 Workington, St Helens Colliery	SER 1248	84

Durham

88

52 Auckland Park, nr Bishop Auckland, Auckland Park Colliery	SER 566	88
53 Beamish, Beamish Colliery, Chop Hill Pit	SER 614	88
54 Beamish, Beamish Colliery, Chop Hill Pit	SER 614a	88
55 Beamish, Beamish Colliery, Mary Pit	SER 615	92
56 Bearpark, Bearpark Colliery	SER 374	92
57 Bearpark, Bearpark Colliery	SER 374a	92
58 Bearpark, Bearpark Colliery	SER 374b	96
59 Burnhope, Burnhope Colliery	SER 515	96
60 Burnhope, Burnhope Colliery, Fortune Pit	SER 375a	96
61 Burnhope, Burnhope Colliery, Fortune Pit	SER 375b	100
62 Burnhope, Burnhope Colliery, Fortune Pit	SER 375c	100
63 Burnhope, Burnhope Colliery, Fortune Pit	SER 378	100
64 Chilton, Chilton Colliery	SER 567	104
65 Craghead, nr Stanley, Oswald Colliery	SER 613	104
66 Dalton, nr Seaham, Sunderland Waterworks, Dalton Pumping Station	SER 372	104
67 Darlington, Darlington Waterworks, Coniscliffe Road, Pumping Station	SER 513	108

FOREWORD
by A. P. Woolrich

George Watkins (1904-1989) spent most of his working life as a heating engineer and boilerman in Bristol. Starting in the 1930s, in his spare time he made short trips throughout Britain photographing and recording stationary steam engines. In 1965, aged 61, he was appointed a research assistant at the Centre for the Study of the History of Technology at Bath University, under Dr R. A. Buchanan, and was enabled to devote all his time adding to and classifying his collection. He was still making field trips until the late 1970s, when ill health made travelling difficult.

He was an occasional contributor to *Model Engineer,* and other periodicals and wrote important papers for the *Transactions of the Newcomen Society.* Following his appointment to Bath University he was in much demand as a lecturer and produced a series of books based on his research. These were:

The Stationary Steam Engine (1968)

The Textile Mill Engine, 2 vol, (1970, 1971), 2ed, (1999)

Man and the Steam Engine, (1975), 2 imp (1978) (with R. A Buchanan)

The Industrial Archaeology of the Steam Engine, (1976) (with R. A. Buchanan)

The Steam Engine in Industry 2 vol, (1978, 1979)

On his death in February 1989 his collection was gifted to the Royal Commission on the Historical Monuments of England. It may be freely consulted at English Heritage's National Record Centre at Swindon. As well as photographs the collection comprises numerous technical notes about all manner of steam engine related topics; an incomparable archive of trade catalogues, some dating from the late nineteenth century; a collection of letters from like-minded friends, of value today for the light they shed on the history of the growth of Industrial Archaeology; lecture notes and slides. His library was left to Bath University.

He would visit a site and take illustrated notes and photographs, usually around half a dozen. His notes usually contained measured sketches of the machines and also the layouts of the premises he visited. In all, he travelled over 120,000 miles and visited nearly 2000 sites, but in approximately 10% only took written notes. He filed sets of contact prints of each visit in binders sorted by engine type and between 1965-1971 he made a selection of the best prints for Bath University staff to print to a larger format. These were drymounted on card and annotated with details from his field notebooks and today form what is known at the Steam Engine Record. It is this collection, with notes, which forms the basis of the present series of regional books.

The Steam Engine Record is filed in numerical order, but catalogues are available listing makers, engine types and locations. When the field trips were being made the historic county names still applied, but the modern catalogues in the Search Room at Swindon allow searching by new counties and metropolitan areas, such as Cleveland and Greater Manchester. In this series, however, the historical county names have been retained.

When he began his surveys, he travelled by bicycle and train, and many were to sites he could reach readily from Bristol, but he soon graduated to a series of autocycles, on which he would pack his photographic gear and his clothing. He planned his trips meticulously during the winter months, writing to mill owners to gain permission, and then during the following summer, (when his boiler was shut down for maintenance), having saved up all his available leave time, would spend two or three weeks on his travels, staying in bed-and-breakfast accommodation, or, as he became more widely known, with friends. During the autumn he would write up his notes, and begin planning the following year's trip.

He was initially interested in beam engines, but soon concentrated on the textile mill engines of mostly Lancashire and Yorkshire. In this he was greatly aided by local experts such as Frank Wightman and Arthur Roberts, who were working in these areas. Later his interest included colliery winding engines, waterworks and marine engines. During the War, when he found difficulty in both travelling far and in getting permission to enter industrial sites, he investigated water-powered sites, such as the Avon Valley brass mills, near Bristol, and the Worcestershire edge tool manufacturing sites. An area of steam technology which did not concern him was the railway locomotive, though he did record a small number of industrial locomotives and traction engines he found on his visits.

The regional distribution of the sites he visited includes most English counties and a number in Wales and Scotland. The numbers of sites he saw in the counties differ greatly, with York-shire, Lancashire, and the counties around Bristol predominating. This is because he had close links with other workers in those areas, and he relied on this network to learn where engines might be found. Areas where he had few contacts tended to be thinly covered.

George Watkins often photographed under near impossible conditions. Engine room lighting was frequently indifferent, and confined space often made hard the siting of the camera for obtaining adequate perspective views. For most of the work reproduced in this series he used a tripod-mounted wooden plate camera with extension bellows which he modified to accept different lenses. In his early years he was continually experimenting with different combinations of film speeds, lenses and exposure times. Although he did eventually own a 35mm roll film camera, he was never happy with using it, and was frequently heard to grumble about the quality of modern film stock.

He used cut film, held in a dark slide, and had the films developed by a local chemist in the centres he visited so he could go back and take another if a print failed. He overcame bad lighting by having very long exposures, so was able to appear in his own prints occasionally.

The long exposures also meant he was able to 'freeze' a slow-moving engine. He did this by shielding the lens by a hand-held card or the lens cap until the engine had reached, say, top dead centre and then removing the shield momentarily. This cumulative exposure resulted in an image of a still engine, and such was his deftness of touch and impeccable timing, that it is very hard to see any kind of shake or blemish on the photographs. He was adept at 'painting with light' – utilising hand-held electric lead-lights with which he could illuminate different parts of the engine successively.

He made copies from his negatives at home for distribution to his friends by using simple contact-print frame and developer chemicals. There are many small sets of his prints in private hands.

The lenses he used were not bloomed to prevent 'flaring' of the image caused by extraneous light from windows or hanging light bulbs, and some of the photographs reproduced are marred by this. He made his selection of prints for the Steam Engine Record on the basis of their historical and technical importance, and not on their artistic quality.

His photographs are a unique record of the end of stationary steam power in this country, being made at a time when electrification, nationalisation and trade depression created wholesale changes in the physical structure of the industrial landscape. They are an invaluable resource to our understanding of the reality of industrial activity, and will interest, as well as the technical historian, the local historian and model-maker. It is good to know they are being published, for this in turn will focus attention on the rest of his reference collection, which deserves to be more widely known and used.

ISSES (The International Stationary Steam Engine Society) is publishing a number of volumes devoted to George Watkins and his work. They will include a short biography, memoirs from several of his friends, a bibliography of his writings and reprints of his articles.

Details may be obtained from:

Mr John Cooper,
73 Coniston Way, Blossom Hill,
Bewdley, Worcestershire,
DYl2 2QA
Tel: 01299 402946

Email:
John.Cooper@isses2.freeserve.co.uk

Web site:
www.steamenginesociety.org

The layout of this book follows the same pattern as the publisher's re-issue of *The Textile Mill Engine*, namely a page of *three* sets of notes followed by three full page photographs illustrating those notes. A little editing has been done to ensure consistency, but the texts are as George Watkins wrote them. It is pointed out, however that they were written over thirty years ago, and were often based on observations made thirty to forty years before that.

The names of locations, sites and makers have been checked where possible, but everything begins with his record in the field notebooks, and in some instances details have changed from what he recorded then to something different now. A mill recorded in particular ownership then may now be known as belonging to a different concern who in fact took it over after his visit. Likewise place names of settlements are not always on modern maps because they have been absorbed into larger places; such has been the pace of urban development. He was also dependent on information, such as the history and dates of engines, from enginemen which later archival research can show to be inaccurate.

Many of the sites, if they now exist at all, have been radically altered and very few of the engines and machines he saw now survive. A handful of engines are preserved in museums, such as the Bradford Industrial Museum, and societies such as ISSES and the Northern Mill Engine Society maintain records of engines in private hands.

The sites are in alphabetical order of place, and then site owner or site name and no attempt has been made to identify them by precise grid references. Each entry heading has an illustration number for this volume, the location details as recorded on the original record card, and the Steam Engine Record (SER) number. This latter number is the key for accessing the copies of the field notebooks and the files of additional photographs in the National Monuments Record at Swindon. The SER number comprises a four digit number (which mirrors the numbering of the field notebooks) and sometimes an additional alphabetical letter. These relate to additional prints of the same site prepared for the mounted set of prints. The photographs in the contact print books and the original negatives are not so numbered. In this volume additional photographs drawn specially from the contact print books series are preceded by CPB then the SER details.

SCOTLAND

George Watkins's travels concentrated on the Scottish industrial heartland, and many of the sites he visited were coalmines. He also saw textile mills, waterworks and water wheels. Scottish builders made a number of the engines he saw.

FURTHER READING

Michael S. Moss & John R. Hume, *Workshop of the British Empire*, 1997

THE NORTHERN ENGLISH COUNTIES
Cumberland
There is only a handful of sites in Cumberland including some relating to mining, steel making and milling.

County Durham
Most of the photographs of sites in Co. Durham relate to collieries. George Watkins made an important survey of the vertical winding engine of the county. These became popular in the North East around *1850*. The cylinder was fixed to the engine-house floor and drove upward to an overhead flywheel on the shaft of which were the winding drums.

The dimensions of the engine would

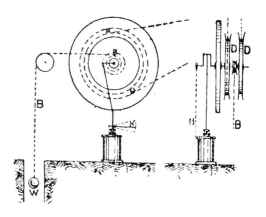

vary with size, but one of the engines at Monkwearmouth (see figure below) had a cylinder of 61 ins diameter and a stroke of 7 ft. The winding drums had a diameter of 22 ft, which when fully wound the rope thickness increased to 25 ft. 23 $^3/_4$ revolutions raised the cage from the bottom to the top of the shaft, 1800 ft deep. The cage had four decks, each deck holding two tubs, which each held 8 $^1/_4$ cwt of coal. The journey time was 1 $^1/_2$ minutes, and it took from 8 to 10 seconds to run the full tubs off and empty tubs on to each tier of the cage, and 6 seconds to start at the beginning of each journey.

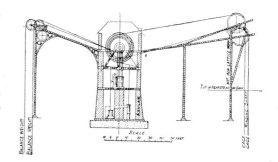

At Monkwearmouth heavy balance-weights, composed of two bunches of chain, each bunch weighing 5 tons, were suspended in a staple pit over two flat pulleys. (See figures at the top and following.) The bunches were attached to a flat chain; each chain wound on a small drum.

This was fixed to the main shaft of the engine, and was 3ft 6 in diameter, rising to 8ft 9 in when the chain was wound up. When the engine began to raise a load of coals both these weights were hanging in the air and assisted the engine by balancing the weight of rope hanging in the shaft. As the engine proceeded and the rope was wound up, the balance weights came to the bottom of the staple pit, and by the time the cage had accomplished half its journey, the flat chain on the small drums was all unwound. As the engine went on, the flat chain was wound up again and before the coals arrived at the pit top the balance weights were raised out of the staple pit and were hanging in the air, tending by their weight to stop the engines, and ready to help the engine on its next journey.

The piston-rod of the engine was guided in a truly vertical direction by means of Crowther's parallel motion, consisting of two beams and a connecting link fastened to the crosshead of the engine as shown in the figure below. Point A was located the distance of the link C, D, E, below the horizontal line running through point B.

A, B, fixed ends of levers, C, D, E, various positions of link; E is the pin passing through the crosshead connecting rod and link; C is the pin connecting lever B to the link; D is the pin connecting lever A to the link.

If the piston is at half stroke, then the pin E is in the middle of the three positions shown C, D, E. If the piston moves upward, the tendency of the lever BC is to pull the cross-head towards B, whilst the tendency of the lever DA is to pull the cross-head towards A. The two tendencies counteract each other, and movement of the piston is thus maintained in a straight line.

In many vertical engines the piston-rod was guided by bars of cast iron, between which the cross-head slid; there was friction between the slide and the bars, and care had to be taken in their adjustment, so they were not so tight as to cause undue friction, nor too loose as to allow perceptible movement of the piston rod.

(Information and figures on the North Eastern vertical winding engines drawn from Arnold Lupton, *Mining*, 1906, chap. XVIII)

A feature of the range of engines George Watkins saw in this area, and also Scotland, was the number of very small plants using steam power. These included a maker of clog-sole blanks, and several large farms where steam was used for threshing and other barn work.

The preservation of steam engines was uncommon when he did the bulk of his survey work, but one engine he saw at Newcastle Museum of Science and Engineering was rescued from a silk mill in Suffolk where he had seen it a number of years previously.

FURTHER READING

George Watkins, 'The Vertical Winding Engines of Durham' *Transactions of the Newcomen Society*, 29, (1953-54 & 1954-55) pp 205-219

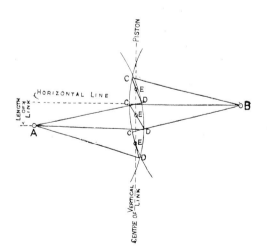

Northumberland

There only a few photographs of sites in Northumberland. Amongst these are several engines used in rural industry such as a sawmill and a barn engine.

Westmorland

George Watkins recorded no sites in the county.

Types of steam engine

Beam engine, the original form as made by Boulton and Watt. This form owed its existence to the fact that all the earlier steam engines were used for pumping water, the beam forming a convenient means of attachment for the pump rods.

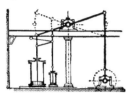

Horizontal Engine, with open frame cast iron bedplate, a type much used for all sizes of engine for general purposes. The bed-plate frame was of a U section, and was bolted down to a foundation of masonry or brickwork, the cylinder, main bearing and guides being bolted to the bed-plate.

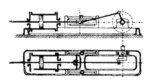

Vertical engine, a type used extensively for both large and small engines; it had the advantage of occupying little floor space. An endless number of varieties of this type was developed, and was the generally accepted type for marine screw-propeller engines.

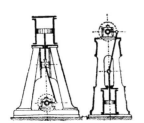

Corliss frame or Girder Engine, a type of horizontal engine. This example had a bored guide, but they were also made with flat-planed guides. In both cases the guides were formed in the main casting or girder which connects the cylinder to the main bearing. There were many varieties of this type.

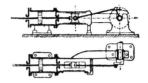

Self contained horizontal engines, with bent or slotted out cranks. This type, largely used for small power short-stroke engines had the cylinder bolted on to the end of an open bedplate, which was widened out at the other end to take both bearings of the crank shaft, so that the flywheel might be keyed on either side. The guides were usually formed in the bedplate, the boring out of the guides and facing of the end flange being done at the same setting.

Oscillating Engines, formerly much used as marine engines. Originally developed for driving paddle wheels, this type has also been used for driving screw propellers. Uncommon in land use.

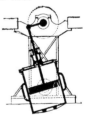

Steeple engine, formerly used for driving paddle wheels. A variety of this type had been used for small powers, and was known as the Table Engine.

Beam Engine, Woolf's Compound. Two unequal cylinders side by side, at one end of the beam. Many pumping engines were of this type.

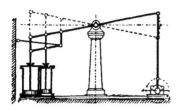

McNaught Compound Beam Engine. This system consisted of a small cylinder (high-pressure cylinder), placed at the opposite end of the beam to the larger cylinder, was introduced by McNaught for increasing the power of existing engines. The high-pressure cylinder was the one added, the original cylinder being the low-pressure cylinder. The power of the engine was thus increased by increase of boiler pressure and the addition of the new small cylinder, to which the boiler was admitted. (See glossary for more details).

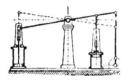

Inclined Frame Engines, used extensively for paddle steamers in several different varieties, usually compound engines.

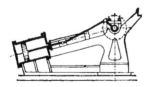

A Double-Cylinder Engine, derived from the above, with the cylinder inclined at an angle of about 45^0, was occasionally used for driving rolling mills in bar iron works.

Radial Engines. (Brotherhood type) A recent type, of which there were many varieties, in both 3 and 4 cylinder configurations. These were used for driving fans, steam launches and other applications requiring speed and compactness.

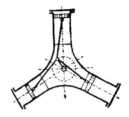

Central Valve Engines (Willans type) A modern design, single acting, compound or triple expansion configuration; a special feature was the hollow piston rod and central valve. Extensively used for driving dynamos coupled direct on to the armature shaft.

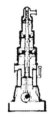

Various ways of arranging cylinders and cranks in double and three-cylinder compound and triple expansion engines

Double cylinder, with cranks at 180^0

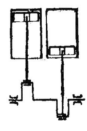

Three-cylinder engine, with cranks at 120^0

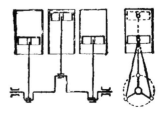

Compound Woolf engine with cranks together

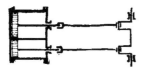

Compound Woolf engine with cranks at 180°

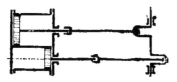

Compound Tandem engine with receiver

Compound engine with cylinders side by side with receiver cranks at 90°

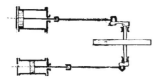

Triple expansion engine with cylinders side by side; cranks at 120°

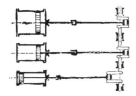

Triple expansion engine, semi-tandem; two cranks at 90°

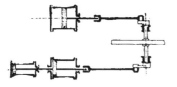

VALVES AND VALVE GEARS

Simple slide valve
This consisted of an inverted metal box sliding on the ported face of the cylinder. It controlled the admission and exhaust of the steam to both ends of the cylinder and exhausted beneath the box valve

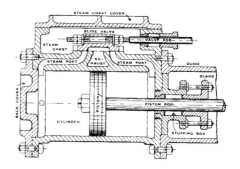

Simple piston valve
This consisted of a turned bobbin, working in a bored liner. It worked on the same principle as the slide valve.

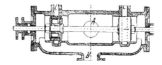

Simple valve gears
These valves were operated by simple eccentric motions of various patterns, and many allowed variable cut-off of the steam as well as reversing.

The Corliss
This was a semi-circular semi-rotating valve working in a bored liner. Separate valves were provided for steam and exhaust at each end of the cylinder, so there were four in number. A trip gear operated the valves.

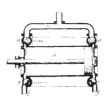

Drop valves

These were circular with taper faces, which fitted upon similar faces fitted to the cylinder. The faces were ground together to make them steam tight. The valves were lifted to admit steam and dropped by the trip gear to cut off the admission. A variety of this pattern was simple bobbins fitted with piston rings.

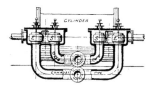

The Uniflow

This had admission valves only since the steam exhausted through a ring of ports in the centre of the cylinder barrel.

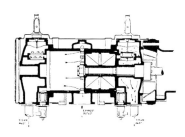

BOILERS

Cornish boilers contained a single flue

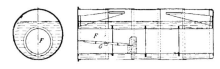

Lancashire boilers contained twin flues

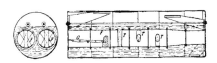

Multitibular boilers were of various types including the locomotive

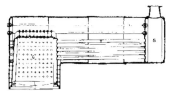

Vertical boilers were of various types. Used in very small plants

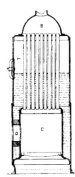

Watertube boilers were of various types.

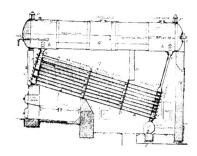

POWER TRANSMISSION

Rope drives, taking power from the engine to the floors of a mill, were usual in textile mills. In older mills power was often transmitted by a vertical shaft.

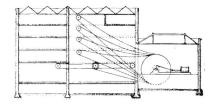

Flat belts of leather or rubberized canvas drove individual machines from a line shaft powered by the rope drive.

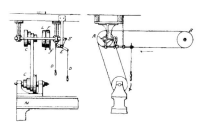

MINING

Winding engines were almost invariably made with two cylinders having cranks at 90^0, allowing good control by the engine driver. A winding engine was required to work intermittently, starting a heavy load from rest, bringing this load up with great velocity, and bringing it to rest again. This had to be done at great speed in a short time, since a great number of winds were needed daily to raise an economic quantity of coal. For this, the engine needed to be powerful and to be under precise control of the engineman at all times.

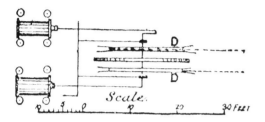

Balancing was done by fixing a rope similar to the winding rope to the bottom of each cage, the rope hanging in a loop down the pit shaft, ensuring a perpetual balance-weight equal to the winding-rope.

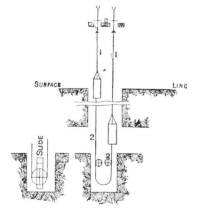

Another method of balancing was by means of the scroll or spiral drum. As the engine proceeded to wind up, the rope was wound in spiral grooves on a continually increasing diameter of drum. The other rope to the descending cage was wound off at an opposing rate so creating a counterbalance. The variation in diameter of the two sides of the drum had the effect of loading the engine proportional to the effort it needed at different stages of the wind.

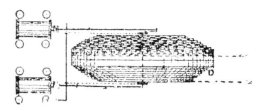

Winding was done by steam, utilising different types of pithead gear.

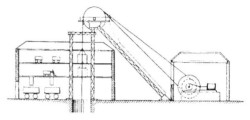

Ventilation was done by various patterns of steam driven rotary fan.

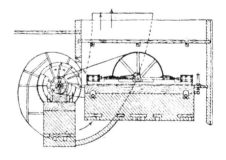

GLOSSARY

Air pump. This removed the condensed water and air contained in the steam. It was normally driven by the engine itself.

Arbor. An axle or spindle.

Barring. This was the action of gently rotating the engine in order to effect adjustments during maintenance. It was done by a lever mechanism which engaged in a series of holes cast in the face or side of the flywheel rim. A variation involved a hand or small steam engine-driven gear engaging in gear teeth cast on the inside of the flywheel rim.

Condensers. these were airtight chambers into which the exhaust steam passed for cooling back to warm water. Cooling was by a jet of cold water, which mixed with the condensate, or, in another pattern of condenser, the cold water passed through a number of small tubes to condense the steam outside them.

Dram or tram. A wheeled tub for conveying coal at the colliery.

Duff coal. Small coal unsuitable for retail sale. Used for firing boilers at collieries.

Economiser. A system of pre-heating boiler feed-water, using the heat of the waste gases in the boiler flues. First invented in 1843 by Edward Green of Wakefield, Yorks.

Edge tools. These were any kind of hand tool with a sharp cutting edge, such as a spade, hoe, sickle or scythe. A slip of toughened steel was forged as a sandwich between softer metal, and then sharpened. This was an ancient craft, some of the sites utilising water-powered tilt hammers.

Egg-ended boiler. A horizontal cylindrical boiler with hemispherical ends and no flues. At early pattern, superseded by the Cornish and Lancashire types.

Flitches. The two halves of the beam of a beam engine. Originally cast solid, beams were sometimes made in two halves and kept apart by spacers and bolts.

Glands. These were recessed bosses in the cylinder cover or valve chest of a steam engine or pump, which were fitted with fibre or metal packing. They allowed the rods to work freely without leaking steam or water.

Governor. This device controlled the speed of the engine, if it was too fast or too slow, by regulating the steam supply. There were many patterns but all depended on rotating weights, which adjusted the control mechanism.

Grid. The National Grid, the national electricity supply system, was begun in the 1920's. Before it became very widespread by the 1950's, many small towns and larger businesses generated their own supplies, with varying supply standards.

Hoppit or hoppet. A large basket used in mining.

McNaughting was patented by William McNaught of Glasgow in 1845. Piston loads were thus opposed, so reducing stresses on the beam centre. The fitting of high-pressure boilers and compound working gave great economy.

Overwinding gear. This was an apparatus to stop a winding engine lifting a cage beyond the pit bank and damaging itself and contents on the pit frame. Various systems were used.

Process steam. This was steam after it had left the engine and before it was condensed. It was used in the plant for other purposes such as central heating, heating dye vats, drying paper.

Rastrick Boiler. A pattern of vertical boiler, which utilised the waste heat from wrought iron-making processes.

Room and Power. The term means that a capitalist established a factory with a power supply (usually steam), and heating, and rented out space to small craftsmen or manufacturers. Each floor had a drive shaft taken from the engine from which individual machines, owned and worked by the tenants, were driven.

Shear. Mechanical scissors used for cropping billets of steel during the rolling process.

Slow banking. This involved the means of controlling the winding engine carefully to allow precise location of the cage at the finish of the wind.

SOURCES

Definitions and illustrations used have been drawn from:

Wilfred Lineham, *A text hook of Mechanical Engineering*, 9ed, 1906.

Arnold Lupton, *Mining*, 3ed, 1906.

Herman Haeder and H. H. P. Powles, *Handbook on the Steam Engine*, 4ed, 1914

More detailed technical information about engine design may be found in:

Colin Bowden, 'The stationary steam engine; a critical bibliography', *Industrial Archaeology Review*, XV, (1992-3), pp 177ff

George Watkins, *The Stationary Steam Engine*, 1968.

George Watkins, *The Textile Mill Engine*, 2 vol, 1970, 1971 (reprinted Landmark Publications, I vol, 1999).

George Watkins, & R A. Buchanan, *Man and the Steam Engine*, 1975, 2ed 1978.

R. A. Buchanan & George Watkins, *The Industrial Archaeology of the Steam Engine*, (1976) This is a very authoritative account of the evolution of design and construction.

George Watkins. *The Steam Engine in Industry*, 2 vol, (1978, 1979). The linking passages describing the application of steam to different industries are specially valuable.

Transactions of the Newcomen Society, especially:
Arnold Throp 'Some notes on the history of the Uniflow Steam Engine', vol 43 (1970-71) pp 19-39

George Watkins, 'The development of the Steam Winding Engine' vol 50, (1978-79), pp 11-24

James L. Wood, 'The introduction of the Corliss Engine into Britain', vol 52, (1980-SI) pp 1-13

R. L. Hills, 'The Uniflow engine, a re-appraisal' Vol 57, (1985-6), pp 39-77

R. W. M. Clouston, 'The development of the Babcock Boiler in Britain up to 1939', vol 58, (1986-87), pp 75-87

James L. Wood. 'The Sulzer steam engine comes to Britain', vol 59, (1987-88), pp 129-152

Stationary Power (the Journal of the International Steam Engine Society), especially:

William D. Sawyer, *Corliss Man and engine*, 2 vol, 1994, (JISSES 10), 1997, (JISSES 13)

Aberdeenshire

1 Inverurie, Thos. Tait & Sons   SER 1270a

Type:	Horizontal twin cylinder
Photo taken:	1966
Maker and Date:	Maker unknown, c 1860s
Cylinder/dimensions:	About 10in x 1ft 3in – slide valves
Hp: 8 – 20	*Rpm:* 60 *Psi:* 80
Service:	Paper glazing machine drive, by gearing to polishing rolls

Although there were electrical drives everywhere else, this engine was retained since it was very little used, and adequate for the glazer drive. It was the only old unit in a well equipped modern works. Fitted with a disc on one crank, and double webbed crank on the other it was a sturdy little engine, again giving good service without even cleaning, since it was so little used. There was nothing to suggest a maker, but it had evidently been in the same place for nearly a century upon a massive stone bed, which must have been as old as the engine.

2 Inverurie, Thos. Tait & Sons   SER 1270b

Type:	Vertical high speed compound
Photo taken:	1966
Maker and Date:	Belliss & Morcom, 1937,
Cylinder/dimensions:	Sizes unknown
Hp: 800	*Rpm:* 333 *Psi:* 200
Service:	Standby power set. Alternator drive

This (No 9332) and a triple expansion Belliss & Morcom engine of 1927 were the main power units, with a total capacity of 1550kW, until they were replaced by a Bellis & Morcom extraction or pass-out turbine of 2,000 kW capacity in 1958. This drove through an alternator by reduction gearing. Steam was supplied to 240 psi by water tube boilers, but the Belliss & Morcom engines were always ready for working as standby sets.

3 Peterculter, nr Aberdeen, Culter Paper Mill   SER 1264

Type:	Horizontal tandem extraction
Photo taken:	1966
Maker and Date:	J. Musgrave & Son, Bolton, 1923
Cylinder/dimensions:	33 $\frac{1}{2}$ in and 49in x 3ft 8in – drop valves
Hp: 2,000	*Rpm:* 112 *Psi:* 160
Service:	Mill drives by shaft and alternator

This was the last complete engine to leave Musgrave's works when they closed in 1926 and Musgrave failed before they could finish it. It was therefore finished and installed by Hick Hargreaves. In a fine granite house especially built for it, it drove the paper-beating mills by an 8in shaft from one end of the crankshaft as well as an 800 kW alternator from the other end. It was fully loaded until 1937 when a 1000 hp Hick turbine was installed assisting with the task. Thereafter, the two units were always working supplying power and low pressure steam to process use, until 1956, when a larger Hick turbine was installed to carry the whole load, with eight J.Thompson, Lancashire boilers rated at 260 psi. The Musgrave engine was then placed on standby, but with increased demand for power, No. 9 boiler was installed.The space for the Musgrave engine would be needed for a larger turbine set by 1972, when it was expected that the engine would be taken out.

3

Angus

4 Dundee, Cleghorn & Co., Arklay Street   SER 1267

Type:	Inverted vertical compound
Photo taken:	1966
Maker and Date:	Thompson, Son & Co., Douglas Foundry, Dundee 1898
Cylinder/dimensions:	15in and 30in x 2ft 6in – Corliss valves
Hp: 300	*Rpm:* 90 *Psi:* 120
Service:	Drove waste jute spinning machinery. 10 ropes to 3 floors from 12ft 6in flywheel

This was a very useful engine, in that the steam was made from jute waste, so burning some fifty tons of refuse per week, until the local authority decided that this was polluting the air and stopped it. This caused costly waste tipping, on municipal sites, and may well have upset the business, from the cost of electric current and the tipping. However, the engine was due to stop in 1967, when it would be scrapped although it was working well. The town site was totally enclosed, with no room for a condensing water cooling pond and no local cold water supply. As a result, an evaporative condenser was fitted, with three banks of inverted "U"-shaped tubes, over which cold water was sprayed, and which was cooled in the tray on the roof. It thus took no space, yet provided a 21in – 22in vacuum regularly. There was also a Belliss & Morcom high speed engine, but this too was to stop when waste refuse oil burning ceased, as firing was too expensive. It was regrettable, as little real nuisance was caused, and the plant would certainly run on with the waste burning. It was almost certainly the last of Thompson's engine at work.

Ayrshire

5 Auchinleck, Highhouse Colliery, No 2 shaft   SER 1252

Type:	Double cylinder horizontal
Photo taken:	1966
Maker and Date:	Grant, Richie, Kilmarnock, 1880s?
Cylinder/dimensions:	20in x 4ft 0in – slide valves
Hp: ?	*Rpm:* 36 *Psi:* 80
Service:	Coal winding 600ft deep. Twin 9ft drums

Plain, simple and fast, this had Stephenson link motion valve gear without a separate cut-off gear. The cylinders, covers and valve chests are completely covered with lagging. The most interesting feature was the very steep angle of the rope lead to the headgear pulleys. This had always been the case, and the wooden headgear survived with this feature in 1967, yet there were no complaints of excess rope wear, usually expected with the sharp bending over the pulleys. Latterly running on 2 Lancashire boilers, the pit at its busiest had 6 egg-end and 6 Lancashire boilers, all of the equipment being steam driven. This pit was expected to close in the 1970s.

6 Mauchline, Mauchline Colliery   SER 1253

Type:	Double cylinder horizontal
Maker and Date:	Kilmarnock Engineering Co., Kilmarnock, date unknown
Cylinder/dimensions:	28in x 5ft 0in – piston valves and drop cut off
Hp: ?	*Rpm:* 32 *Psi:* 120
Service:	Coal winding. Shaft 600ft deep, 2 ½ tons per wind. Drum 12ft 6in

The makers are little known, and this was the only engine made by them I met. They may have had associations with Andrew Barclay & Co., of the same town, but the cut-off gear was similar to Wood of Wigan. The wind was made in 19 revolutions of the engine. It appeared to be a late design, possibly of the early 1900s, which had been altered very little. The shaft headgear was of steel lattice design, and again suggested the same dating. When there were two winding engines and colliery electrical generating plant there had been 7 Lancashire boilers, but latterly with Grid supply of current and a single winding engine, only three were left. It was due to close in 1966.

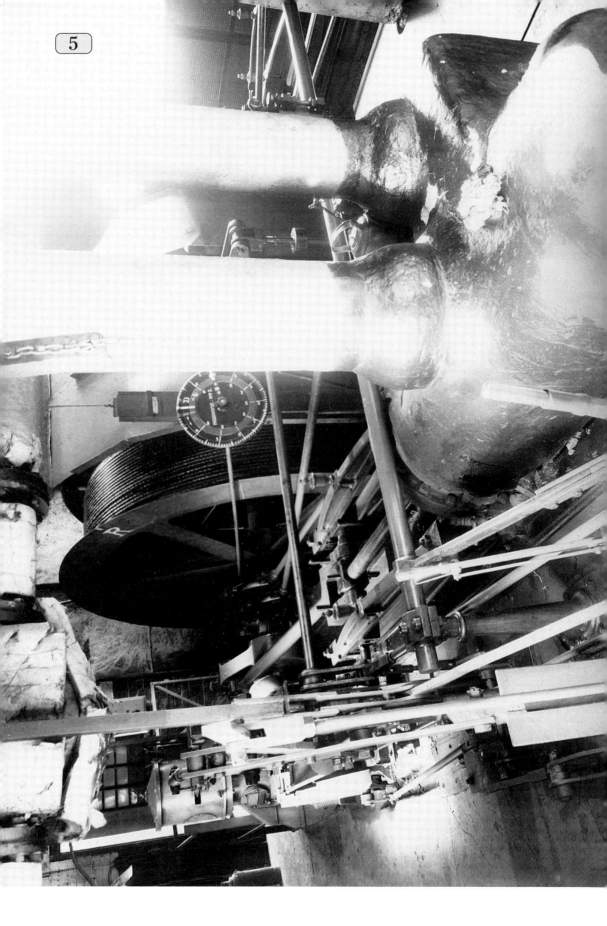

4

7 New Cumnock, Knockshinnock Colliery   SER 1251

Type:	Double cylinder horizontal
Photo taken:	1966
Maker and Date:	John Wood, Wigan, 1918?
Cylinder/dimensions:	22in x 4ft 0in – piston valves and drop cut off
Hp: ?	*Rpm:* 36 *Psi:* 120
Service:	Coal winding. Shaft 630ft deep

The shaft was finished in 1940, and the engine was second-hand from an unknown colliery. It was Wood's usual type, with drop cut-off valves operated from the valve tail rod, which lifted and dropped it twice per revolution. The winding cycle again was fast, winding in 25 seconds, with 10 seconds for banking, and often this was reduced to 32 seconds per wind. There were two tubs per cage. Two hand-fired Lancashire boilers allowed for 160 psi, actually worked at 120 psi for the engine. Gooch link motion was fitted as were metallic packings to all of the valve and piston rod glands. The colliery was expected to run into the 1970s.

Berwickshire

8 Duns, Laidlaw's, Cumledge Blanket Mills   SER 1049

Type:	Horizontal single tandem condensing
Photo taken:	1961
Maker and Date:	Douglas & Grant, Kirkcaldy, 1914
Cylinder/dimensions:	21in & 40in x 4ft 0in – drop valves
Hp: 500	*Rpm:* 100 *Psi:* 150
Service:	Woollen mill drive. Direct drive to mill shaft

This replaced an earlier engine, and was in a separate engine house by the mill. The drive was by an overhead extension shaft from the crankshaft, to the old second motion shaft within the mill. The shaft over the yard was 4 $^1/_2$ ins diameter, and split in the mill to drive by bevel wheels to other parts. A typical Douglas & Grant engine, it gave no trouble until the mill was converted to motor drive in the early 1960s when the engine was scrapped, still in perfect condition.

Clackmannan

9 Alloa, Polmaise Colliery, No 4 Shaft   SER 1271a

Type:	Double cylinder horizontal
Photo taken:	1966
Maker and Date:	Grant, Ritchie, Kilmarnock, No 458, 1903
Cylinder/dimensions:	26in x 5ft 0in – slide valves
Hp: ?	*Rpm:* 50 *Psi:* 100
Service:	Wound coal from 1270ft. 2 tons per wind

The notable feature of Polmaise was the very steep rope angles, almost 60 degrees. This was always considered to increase rope wear and reduce the life, but there was no complaint here, where the shafts and engines were always the same. Although the engines were not small they certainly ran at higher speed than most, i.e. up to 50 rpm maximum. No expansion gear was fitted, and the engines were driven entirely on the indicators, the driver being in front of the drum, out of sight of the pit bank. In later years this engine was winding men and materials, and so restricted to 36ft. per second maximum. The colliery appeared to be carrying on with the steam sets No. 3 and 4; the new electric winder on No. 6 shaft not having been used.

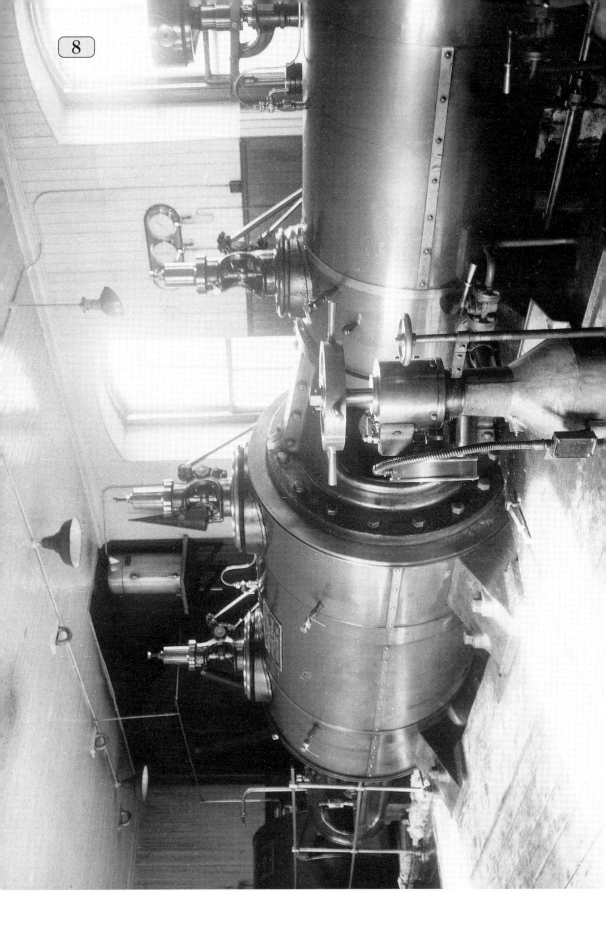
8

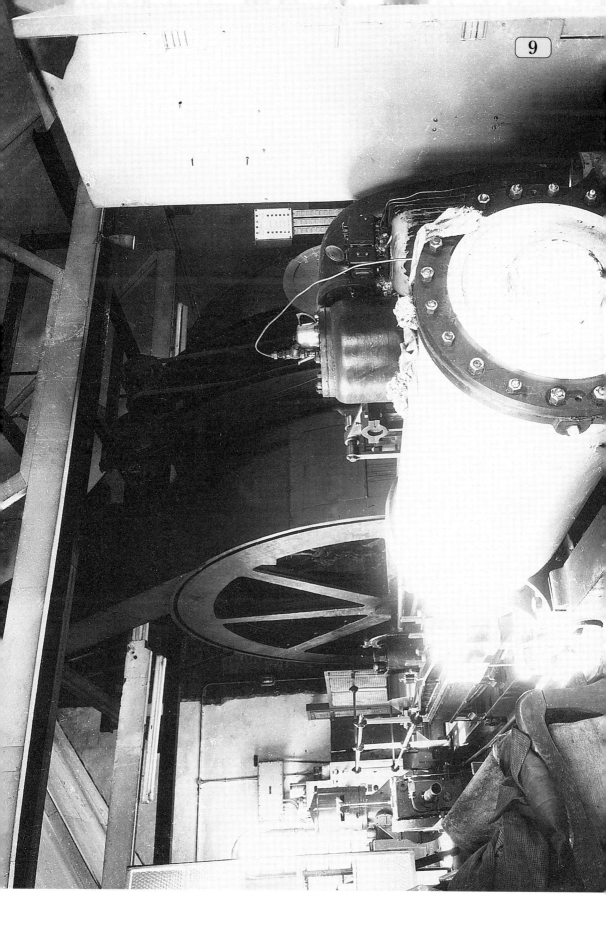

9

10 Alloa, Polmaise Colliery, No 5 Shaft   SER 1271b

Type:	Double cylinder horizontal
Photo taken:	1966
Maker and Date:	G. Inglis & Co., Airdrie 1922
Cylinder/dimensions:	30in x 5ft 0in – Corliss valves
Hp: ?	*Rpm:* 49 *Psi:* 100
Service:	Shaft sinking, from 1,000ft, to 1,800ft. Shaft 16ft diameter

This was first at a pit at Douglas, Lanarkshire until about 1930, having been used for sinking there. It therefore had only a single rope and hoppit, and this was continued at Polmaise where it was again used for sinking only. It was a modern and powerful engine, with the cylinder centres very wide apart, i.e. some 24ft, but with only a single drum, and a long unused section on the shaft. It was fitted with Whitehead Corliss trip gear, unusual for a winder. It was thus a massive modern unit, which had never had a chance to do its work with two cages in balance, since in sinking only a single rope is used as a rule. It was used as the shaft required in 1968. There were four Babcock boilers for 150 psi, which also fed the turbine generating plant.

Dumfriesshire

11 Kirkconnell, Fauldhead Colliery, No 3 Shaft   SER 1250

Type:	Double cylinder horizontal
Photo taken:	1966
Maker and Date:	Andrew Barclay & Co., Kilmarnock, No 6676
Cylinder/dimensions:	24in x 4ft 6in – slide valves
Hp: ?	*Rpm:* 36 *Psi:* 90
Service:	Coal winding. 450 feet deep to splint coal

Again a plain engine with nothing to distinguish it, this was very fast, and the large shaft, which allowed the cages to carry four tubs in a square on a single deck, permitted up to 600 winds to be made in 7 $\frac{1}{2}$ hours. The engine made 13 revolutions per wind, with a 12ft drum. The original single drum was altered in 1963, to one with twin drums and a central braking track. The cylinders were re-bored in 1960. It was expected that it would work out the coal reserves, the colliery probably closing in the early 1970s. The boiler plant was very unusual comprising two Yarrow, and two Babcock, water tube units.

East Lothian

12 Dunbar, Sir James Hope's Estate, East Barns Farm   SER 1294

Type:	Horizontal single cylinder, non-condensing
Photo taken:	1967
Maker and Date:	James Skedd, Dunbar Foundry? c. 1860s
Cylinder/dimensions:	10in x 1ft 6in – slide valves
Hp: 20	*Rpm:* 60 *Psi:* 80
Service:	Barn machinery drive 8in belt drive, off pulley

A mid-Victorian country-made engine, this was the simplest possible design, placed with the boiler and coal store in a separate building on the side of the main barn. The exhaust steam was used to heat the boiler feed water, and may have been used for cattle feed cooking in the barn. It certainly had been greatly used, as the stone steps up to the engine from the stoking floor (the boiler was separated by a stone wall) were deeply worn. Barn threshing was standard so far north where harvests were late, and wet weather prevented dry harvesting. Some of the machinery had been removed, but had comprised threshing, crusher, kibbler and root cutter, etc., for a very large estate, latterly much reduced in size. A large area of potatoes was grown in later years, and with less cattle, barn work was reduced. The engine was long disused but in position in 1969.

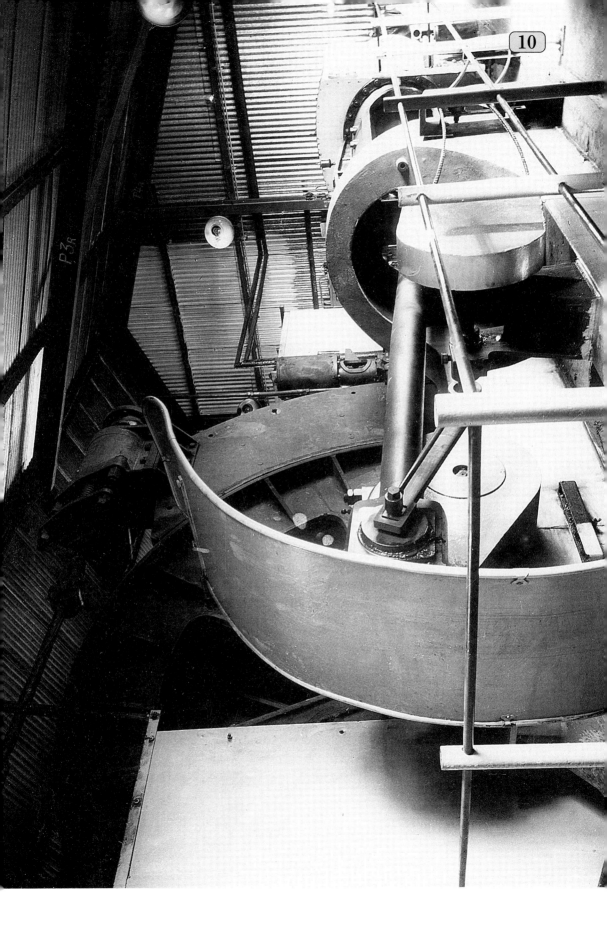

13 Tranent, nr Edinburgh, Fleets Colliery   SER 560

Type:	Cornish beam
Photo taken:	1953
Maker and Date:	Perran Foundry, Cornwall, 1847
Cylinder/dimensions:	50in bore – about 10ft 0in stroke
Hp: No data	*Rpm:* No data *Psi:* No data
Service:	Pit pump

This ran for just a century, and at the site was thought to have been moved from Dolphinstone Colliery, but no date was known. It was interesting for the fluted side pipes between the upper and lower valve chests, also there was a flanged entry on one of the side pipes here, as at Preston Grange, which are rare features on Cornish engines. Fleets was of interest for some good panelling in the engine room and on the cylinder case. The whole was probably scrapped in the early 1960s.

14 Tranent, nr Edinburgh, Prestongrange Colliery   SER 561

Type:	Cornish beam
Photo taken:	1953
Maker and Date:	Harvey & Co., Hayle, Cornwall, 1874
Cylinder/dimensions:	70in x 12ft 0in (10ft at pumps)
Hp: No data	*Rpm:* No data *Psi:* No data
Service:	Colliery pump

This was supplied new to the colliery by Harvey in 1874, and ran regularly until 1951. King post stays were added to the beam later, possibly in the 1930s. It was a standard Harvey engine, but there were two interesting points: i.e. there appeared to be no air pump bucket fitted; also there was a flange on the side of the equilibrium trunk, but it was not known if this received low pressure steam from another engine at one time, or whether it fed steam to a low pressure turbine. It will probably be the only Cornish engine left in a coal mine. The absence of top brasses in the end of the beam will be noted; single acting engines did not need them.

Lanarkshire

15 Glasgow, Beardmore, (Wm) & Co., Parkhead Forge   SER 1047a

Type:	Horizontal twin cylinders – non condensing
Photo taken:	1961
Maker and Date:	Duncan Stewart & Co., 1942
Cylinder/dimensions:	42in x 5ft 0in – piston valves
Hp: 8000	*Rpm:* 120 *Psi:* 120
Service:	Steel rolling mill. Double reduction to billets and triple reduction to 15ft wide sheet mill

This was a replica from the same drawings of the original engine of 1891 which failed when urgently needed, after very heavy overloading. This, too, had been fully worked but the 15 ft wide armour plate mill which was driven through triple reduction gearing was dismantled in 1951, and the housings sent to a Sheffield mill. Three modern water tube boilers provided steam at 220 psi, which was fed to the steam hammers and rolling mill through large reducing valves and accumulators; that for the mill engine was 36 ft high by 10 ft diameter. It worked very well with the massive reducing valves into the receivers. Exhaust was to atmosphere. Production was stainless steel billets for Sheffield in the 1960s, the steel was made in Glasgow as ingots of 22in x 24in sections, which were reduced in the mill to 15in x 7in in five minutes.

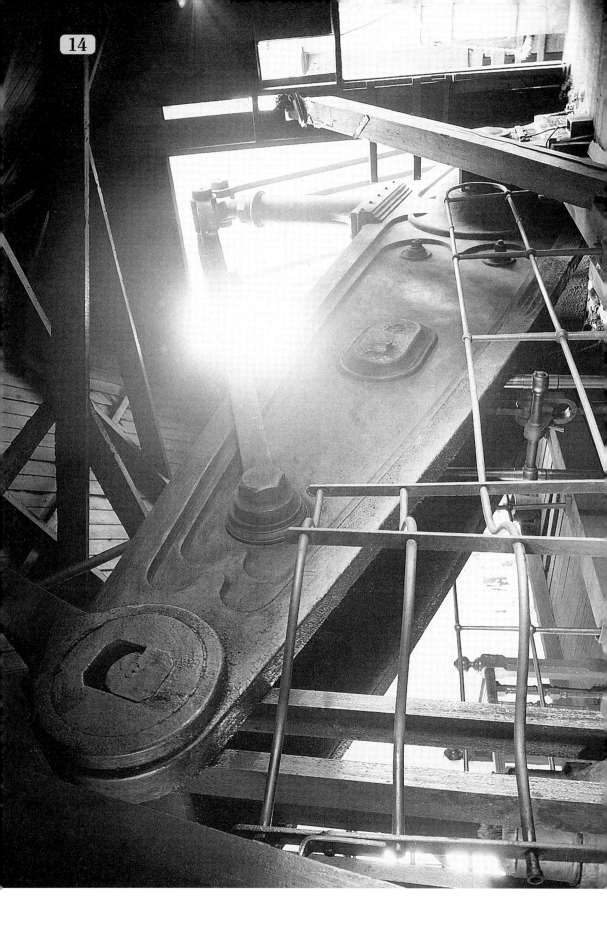

16 Glasgow, Beardmore, (Wm) & Co., Parkhead Forge   SER 1047b

Type:	Inverted vertical twin cylinder.
Photo taken:	1961
Maker and Date:	Maker unknown, c. 1892
Cylinder/dimensions:	About 15in x 1ft 6in – slide valves
Hp: ?	*Rpm:* 90 *Psi:* 120
Service:	Heavy shears drive. Double gear reduction to cutter.
	Total ratio about 12 to 1.

Although very massive, the heavy duty needed led to many small failures in this shear, the engine and the framing suffering badly. Following a complete breakdown of the framing, its loss was such that it was completely rebuilt with heavier framing, and overhaul of the engine itself. The result was well worth while, and with care gave very good results. The engine was a sound design, with counterbalanced cranks, large bearings, cylinders, piston rods and motion generally. Ingot shearing is very heavy duty, and the high power of the engine, plus the high reduction ratio of the gearing puts great stress upon the framing. It was still used in 1973.

17 Glasgow, The Kingston Dock Swing Bridge   SER 1273

Type:	Double cylinder horizontal
Photo taken:	1966
Maker and Date:	John Yule, Glasgow, 1867
Cylinder/dimensions:	7 $\frac{1}{2}$ in x 1ft 6in – twin piston valves
Hp: 20?	*Rpm:* 80 *Psi:* 60
Service:	Road bridge over river entry to Kingston Dock

This was closed with Kingston Dock in 1967, to be replaced with a fixed bridge. It was a very unusual layout, with the bridge members running on large rollers, the whole being turned on a rack upon the side of the dock wall, by a pinion driven by the engine; the engine, boiler, and engine driver, all moving with the bridge itself. The print shows the boiler attached to the bottom of the bridge members (seen overhead), the driver sitting upon a platform at the other end to fire and drive the engine. Even the engine was unusual in that it had separate piston valves at each side of the cylinder, one for steam and the other for the exhaust, so having two sets of link reversing motion to each cylinder. The funnel was carried up at the side of the bridge. It was a quaint layout that one wished might have been retained as it was unique.Latterly heavy traffic, too fast, had led to extensive stiffening throughout, for which it was not designed.

18 Glasgow, The Kingston Dock Swing Bridge   SER 1273a

Type:	Steam driven swing bridge
Photo taken:	1966
Maker and Date:	Usual data not applicable, see below
Service:	Road passage over dock entry

The bridge was built by David Yule of Glasgow in 1867 to provide passage across the small Kingston dock (then heavily used by small coasting vessels called puffers) with a double traffic lane. Traffic density and weight greatly increased over the years and latterly in some respects the bridge was more strengthening than original metal, but nonetheless served until, with the cessation of coastal vessel traffic, the dock was closed and filled in to become part of the new through roadway. The pivot and turning mechanism was at the far end of the bridge, with the boiler chimney (which can be seen smoking) coming up the side. It was a simple swing bridge, a typical piece of good Glasgow work, which after a century of service, in its old age, carried at least four times its initial loadings. It was scrapped in 1967. It took about 1 $\frac{1}{2}$ minutes to open the bridge from placing the road barriers.

19 Glasgow, Lean & Co., Muslin Manufacturers, Reid Street SER 555

Type:	Double McNaught beam
Photo taken:	1953
Maker and Date:	Turnbull, Grant & Jack, Canal Bank Foundry, Glasgow, 1858 & 1871
Cylinder/dimensions:	24in x 2ft 0in and 28in x 4ft 0in – slide valves
Hp: 250	*Rpm:* 36 *Psi:* 55
Service:	Mill drive. Muslin manufacturers

The two sides were similar although one was erected 11 years after the other. The drives to the mill were all by gearing and extensive, as part of the mill was 4, another 5 floors high, and in the weaving shed (single floor only) were 23 pairs of bevel wheels for the loom shaft drives. There was 4,750 ft of shafting altogether, from 7in diameter downward, but with it all the friction was about 70 hp, by no means excessive. The initial drive from the flywheel rim was by beechwood teeth, and when the mills were converted to electric driving in 1957 much of the shafting was scrapped.

20 Glasgow, Rank, (Jos), & Co., flour mill, Shearer Street   SER 1289

Type:	Inverted vertical triple expansion
Photo taken:	1967
Maker and Date:	Wood Bros. & Marsden's, 1926?
Cylinder/dimensions:	19 $^1/_2$ in – 32in and 49in x 3ft 6in – Corliss valves
Hp: 1600	*Rpm:* 80 *Psi:* 180
Service:	Flour mill drive by 35 ropes off 18ft 6in flywheel

This was designed by Wood Bros., and although Mr. Rank insisted, they could not complete the engine and this was done by Marsden's. The date was uncertain but late in the 1920s. It was thus Wood Bros. in all ways, with each engine, the high, intermediate and the low pressure, separate with a coupling between each crank section. There was a steel column to each engine, and the bed sections as seen at the right hand side. It was tragic that the mill fire caused the loss of this engine afterwards, as a considerable sum was spent on it just before the fire, to provide a new supply of cooling water for it when Kingston Dock, the usual source, was closed. It would have been the last Wood Bros. engine in regular use, and one of the last that they were associated with.

21 Glasgow, Templeton & Co., No 7 carpet mill   SER 1257

Type:	Single cylinder horizontal non-condensing
Photo taken:	1966
Maker and Date:	Fullerton, Hodgart & Barclay, Paisley 1900
Cylinder/dimensions:	18in x 3ft 0in – Corliss valves
Hp: 100	*Rpm:* 88 *Psi:* 100
Service:	Mill plant drive by 2 - 12in belts, from 12ft flywheel and 12in belt to generator

This was steamed by a Yarrow boiler at 220 psi and exhausted into the works process heating system at 10 psi. It thus cost very little to run, but was due to be scrapped in the late 1960s when a complete changeover to Grid current in all of the remaining Templeton's mills was intended. This had given very little trouble, with no major breakdowns or repairs. The weaving shed drive was interesting as the shafts over the looms were driven by belts from a single pulley, with belts to the other shafts. It was actually intended to close No. 7 completely and transfer the work to another plant. It was possibly the last Fullerton Hodgart & Barclay engine at work in a mill.

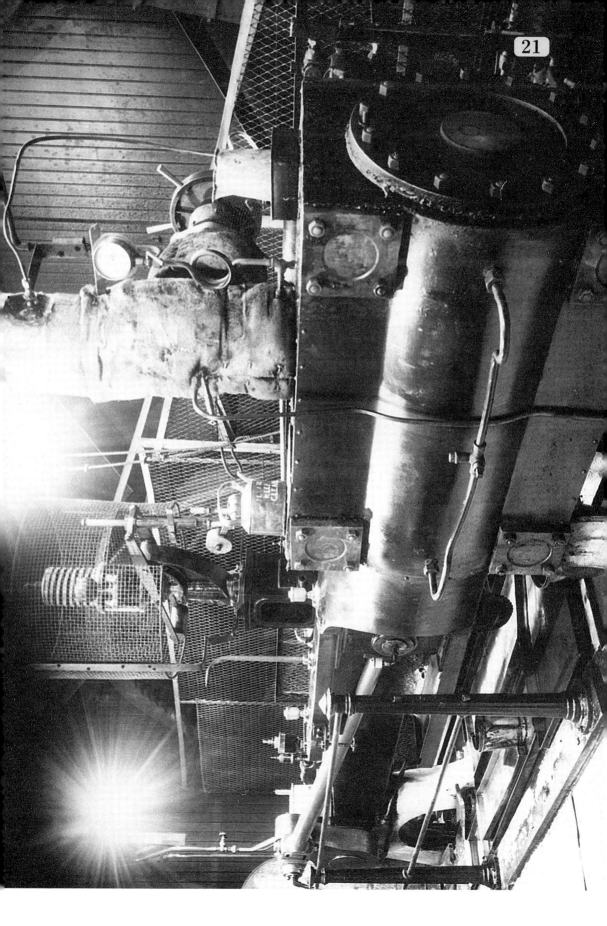

22 Newmains, Kingshill Colliery, No 2 Shaft   SER 1255

Type:	Double cylinder horizontal
Maker and Date:	Shearer & Pettigrew, 1914
Cylinder/dimensions:	24in x 4ft 6in – slide valves
Hp: ?	*Rpm:* 25 *Psi:* 110
Service:	Coal winding. Shaft 1320ft deep. Drum 14ft 6in diameter

This was a late sinking, the No. 2 shaft not being finished until 1926. No. 2 was plain, but quite powerful, with a large drum for the size of the cylinders. The engine remained unaltered, but the drum may have been replaced by one built up in steel. There were 4 boilers, 3 on for the two winders, hand fired with waste coal, and the shaft headgears were made of rolled steel sections. Kingshill was a part of the Coltness Coal and Iron Co., plants, an example of how an old concern kept up to date by sinking new pits as the old were worked out. There was probably never any generating plant here, as many of the pits were linked into central schemes.

23 Riddoch Hill, Riddoch Hill Colliery   SER 1256

Type:	Double cylinder horizontal
Photo taken:	1966
Maker and Date:	Maker unknown, rebuilt 1960
Cylinder/dimensions:	20in x 5ft 0in – piston valves
Hp: ?	*Rpm:* 60 *Psi:* 120
Service:	Coal winding. 1000ft deep, skip winding fitted 1960

Another old pit rejuvenated, the engine was completely rebuilt (only the engine beds being left) by John Wood of Wigan at the changeover to skip winding, and the whole was extremely efficient afterwards. The skips carried 2ton 5cwt coal per trip, and the cycle was winding 40 seconds, and top and bottom banking 20 seconds, making a 60 second cycle from the official depth of 978ft. The exhaust was to atmosphere. There were latterly 3 boilers, 2 in use at a time with duff coal (hand fired) which is a waste product, with no marketing value. The pit seemed likely to continue in operation, but even sound older pits were scrapped to provide load for expensive new sinkings, which were often making heavy losses.

24 Stepps, nr Glasgow, Cardowan Colliery   SER 1445

Type:	Double cylinder horizontal
Photo taken:	1972
Maker and Date:	Murray & Paterson, Coatbridge, 1924
Cylinder/dimensions:	26in x 5ft 0in – piston valves
Hp: ?	*Rpm:* 36 *Psi:* 120
Service:	Coal winding, shaft 2,040 feet full depth, rope drum 18 feet diameter. 3 tons per trip

There were two identical engines, new when the shafts were sunk in the 1920s, but No. 2 shaft was only 720 feet deep, where most of the coal had been worked. Barclay drop cut-off were fitted originally, driven by the piston valve tail rods, but had been taken off. No. 1 engine had piston tail rods, but these were never fitted to No. 2. The driver was between the two cylinders working entirely on the depth indicators. The reversing engines were unusual, since they were placed at the side to the rear of the engines, as can be seen in the lower left hand corner. The chests for the drop cut-off valves were left in place and simply blanked off. The pit was due to close in 1972, and the equipment was being wound out in August.

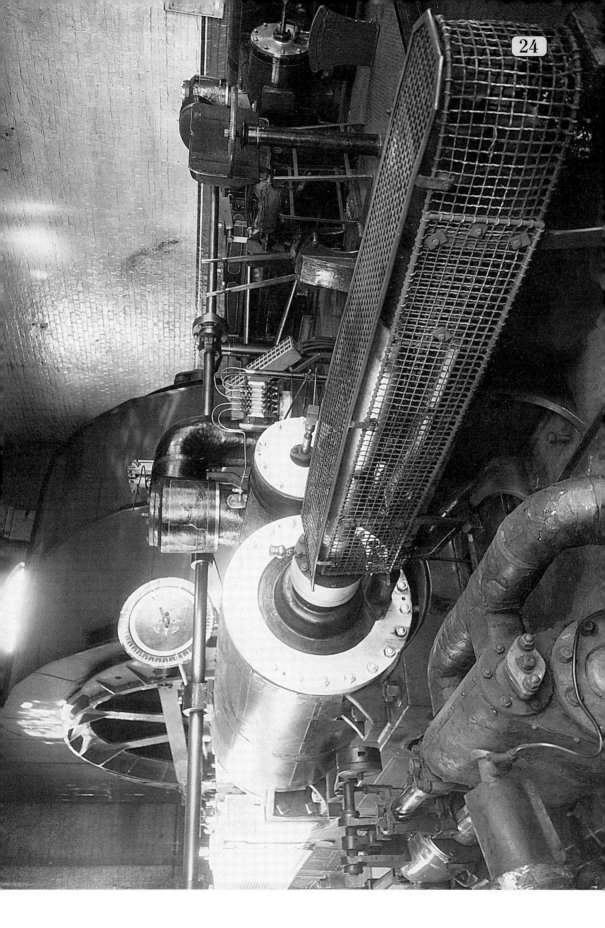

24

25 Whitrigg, Whitrigg Colliery, No 5 shaft   SER 1254a

Type:	Double cylinder horizontal
Photo taken:	1966
Maker and Date:	Gibb, Hogg & Barclay, Airdrie, 1909
Cylinder/dimensions:	26in x 5ft 0in – piston valves
Hp: ?	*Rpm:* 40 *Psi:* 140
Service:	Coal winding, shaft 1150ft deep. Rope drum 16ft 0in diameter

This was built with slide valves, the piston valve cylinders being fitted at an unknown date, possibly when higher boiler pressure was adopted for electrical generating. The steam valve chests were cast in one with the cylinders. The wind was made in 21 revolutions, with the steam cut off entirely after 13 revolutions when the cage reached the maximum speed of 38 mph. It was a well equipped pit, with 2-750 kW mixed pressure turbo-generators and a 500 kW Belliss & Morcom engine, all of this being scrapped in 1965. The pit seemed likely to run for a few years, but with heavy closures in Scotland , there was doubt everywhere. Many Scottish pits were highly efficient, with the winder exhaust steam used for electricity generating. The coal Board policy of scrapping economically viable plant and wasting the steam to the atmosphere was inexplicable. It wasted millions of tons of coal, and a great deal of money, but it was general with the N.C.B. on nationalisation.

26 Whitrigg, Whitrigg Colliery, No 5 shaft   SER 1254b

Type:	Horizontal double cylinder
Photo taken:	1966
Maker and Date:	Inglis & Co., Airdrie, date unknown
Cylinder/dimensions:	7in x 1ft 0in – slide valves
Hp: 20	*Rpm:* 100 *Psi:* 140
Service:	Rope fitting capstan engine

This provided three winding speeds, through the gearing, which was fitted with jaw clutches, to the rope drum which was 6ft diameter. It was a plain local type engine, which provided a great hauling capacity from small cylinders. An interesting feature was that the ropes were wound on the drum in two layers. It was very useful and gave high lifting capacity for extra heavy machinery handling in the shaft.

Midlothian

27 Dalkeith, Smeaton Mines   SER 562a

Type:	Horizontal, condensing tandem
Photo taken:	1953
Cylinder/dimensions:	About 18in and 28in x 4ft 6in – slide valves
Hp: Disused, no data	*Rpm:* Disused, no data *Psi:* Disused, no data
Service:	Abandoned drift mine, seams worked out. Engine named *Caledonia*

The seams were worked out and the whole abandoned in 1951, but it had been a busy pit, as this engine had often pulled 1,000 tons per day up the drift of 1 in 3 from the working faces. It was an endless rope system, in which the engine ran continuously in one direction, driving a single traction pulley from which the rope went to the pit bottom and returned around a lower pulley, the loaded drams being clipped on to the rope to pull them to the top. The engine was similar to a mill engine and highly economical as it ran with a condenser. There were 7 other engines and 8 boilers at the pit.

28 Dalkeith, Smeaton Mines   SER 562b

Type:	Double cylinder, horizontal, non-condensing
Photo taken:	1953
Maker and Date:	Inglis & Co., Airdrie, date unknown
Cylinder/dimensions:	20ft x 2ft 6 ins – slide valves
Hp: 100	*Rpm:* 100 *Psi:* 80
Service:	Coal hauling from working faces

This also hauled up the 1 in 3 incline from the pit, but by a main and tail rope. In this there were two rope drums, one each for the main haulage rope and the tail rope. The coal was pulled by the heavier main rope and the light tail rope pulled the drams back at points where the road rose instead of falling, as this went farther into the pit than SER 562a. It was an interesting layout, as, beside brakes, this engine was fitted with change-over valves so that as it was lowering empty drams, the engine acted as an air compressor, so resisting the lowering load usefully by feeding air back into the coal cutter's air system.

29 New Craighall, Newcraighall Colliery, No 3 shaft   SER 1293

Type:	Double cylinder horizontal
Photo taken:	1967
Maker and Date:	Grant, Ritchie, 1903
Cylinder/dimensions:	25in x 5ft 0in – slide valves
Hp: ?	*Rpm:* 50 *Psi:* 100
Service:	Coal winding, 800ft deep, 14ft drum

This was a well equipped unit under private enterprise, with 2 winders, electrical generating plant, and fan, then using 8 or 9 of the 13 boilers. Under nationalization this was down to one winder, no generators, and 5 boilers fired by waste duff coal and a standby steam fan. Barclay's drop cut-off valves were fitted before the valve chests, and this was almost certainly added later, but was latterly disused. It was a plain engine, again well used and cared for. It was replaced by an electric winder but the engine is preserved in Scotland .

30 Newtongrange, Lady Victoria Colliery   SER 1290

Type:	Double cylinder horizontal.
Photo taken:	1967
Maker and Date:	Grant, Ritchie, Kilmarnock, 1907
Cylinder/dimensions:	42in x 7ft 0in – drop valves
Hp: ?	*Rpm:* 60 *Psi:* max 100
Service:	Coal winding, shaft 1620 feet deep

This was the largest engine surviving in Scotland , although there were others as large until 1970. It wound 7tons 4 cwt of coal per wind from 1620ft at a maximum speed of 57ft per second. It was likely to remain in use for some years, possibly to work out the coal. Expansion gear under governor control was used, with the driver cutting off all steam at 17 of the total of 26 revolutions. Always heavily loaded, it had its share of mishaps, as the left hand bed was patched, and the right hand cylinder also had been replaced. It was certainly fully worked in the late 1960s, and well looked after. The drum was parallel 20ft diameter, and pulled 8 drams of coal on two cage decks per wind. It was said to develop some 1600 peak horse power. There were 18 boilers in all, for the turbine generators and air compressors.

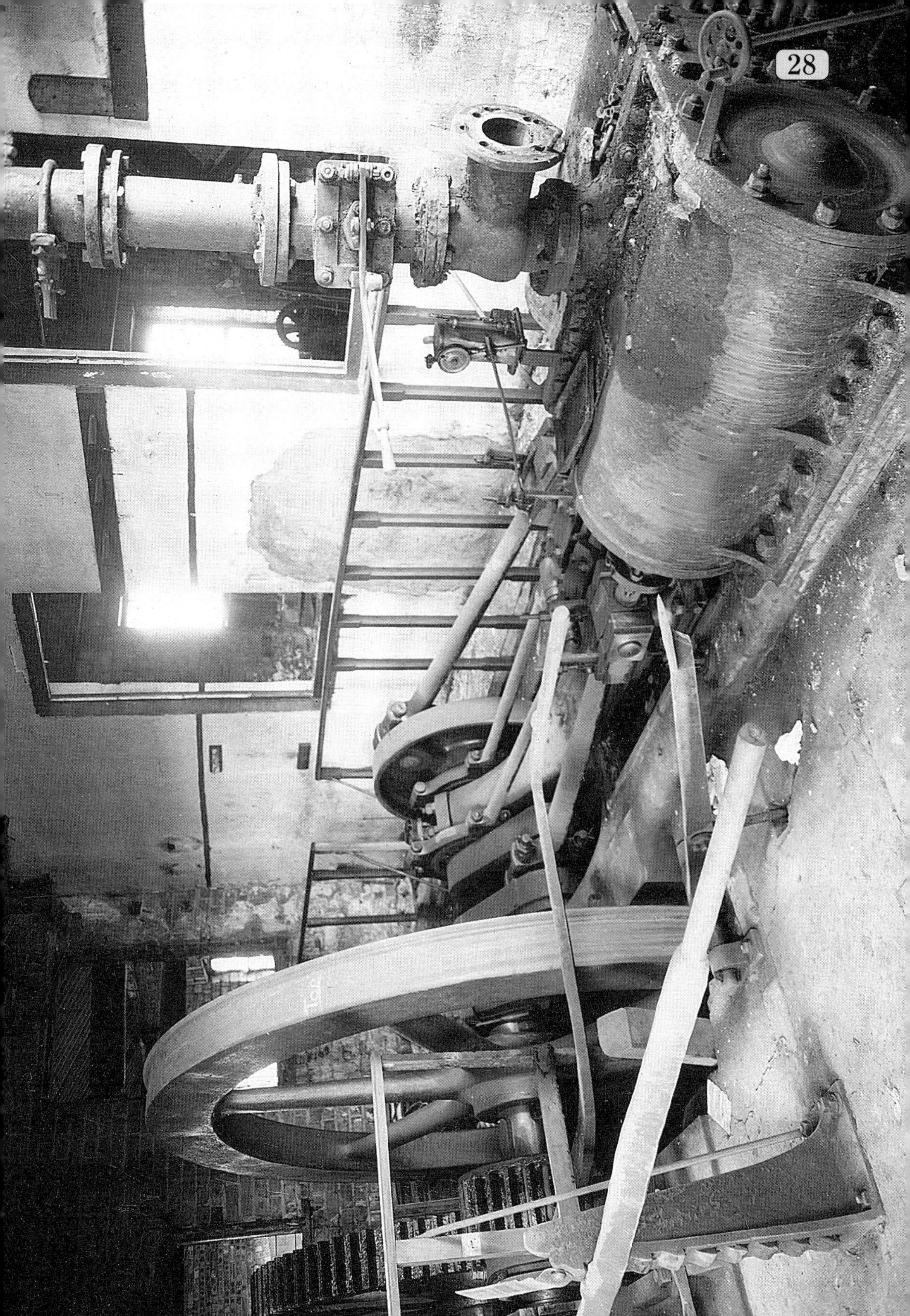

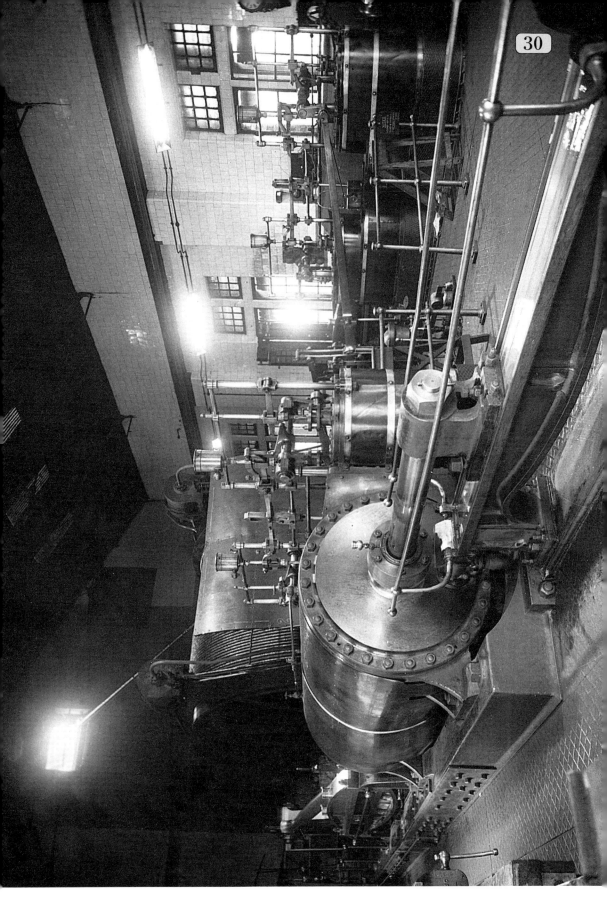

31 Newtongrange, Lingerwood Colliery SER 1291

Type:	Double cylinder horizontal
Photo taken:	1967
Maker and Date:	J Aitken & Co., 1891
Cylinder/dimensions:	22 $^1/_4$ in x 5ft 0 in – Slide then drop valves
Hp: ?	*Rpm:* 38 *Psi:* 100
Service:	Coal winding, shaft 800ft deep, 12ft drums

The colliery was abandoned in 1968 when the photograph was taken, with the winding engine in superb condition, but no ropes on. The colliery was always heavily worked, with two decks in the cage with 1 x 1 ton tub in each, making the wind in 55 seconds. The heaviest working ever was in 1952 when up to 1148 tubs per shift were wound, with an annual output of 240,000 tons. The original slide valve cylinders were replaced in 1911 by the drop valve ones seen, by Grant, Ritchie, possibly when the boilers were renewed. The cylinders were re-bored in 1935 and the tail rods seen were fitted in 1953. It was thus heavily used and well cared for, and certainly paid its way. The pit was adjacent to Lady Victoria (SER 1290).

32 Roslin, Roslin Colliery SER 1292a

Type:	Double cylinder horizontal.
Photo taken:	1967
Maker and Date:	Inglis & Co., Airdrie, 1912
Cylinder/dimensions:	26 $^1/_2$ in x 5ft 0in – piston valves
Hp: ?	*Rpm:* 50 *Psi:* 100
Service:	Coal winding, shaft 960ft deep, rope drum 12ft diameter

Another well-used and cared for Lothian engine, this had the original valve chests refitted when new cylinders were put on by Inglis 1954. It raised 57 cwt of coal per wind, and did this in 40 seconds, and certainly was very fast in getting away. The engine took steam for 18 of the 25 revolutions the wind required.

33 Roslin, Roslin Colliery SER 1292b

Type:	Electro–hydraulic, drive unit
Photo taken:	1967
Maker and Date:	McTaggart & Co., c 1960
Cylinder/dimensions:	3 x 40 hp motors
Hp: 120	*Rpm:* 30 *Psi:* (drum)
Service:	Man winding, 960ft deep

This was a completely modern and not very useful unit since at the speed of l5ft per second it took over 60 seconds for the wind, with 8 men per trip, which was relatively slow for getting men out quickly in an emergency. The men certainly disliked it, although it was better than nothing. It comprised three motor-driven pumping units supplying oil under pressure to the hydraulic power cylinder or motor seen at the right hand side of the winding drum. It probably served as a haulage engine previously, where the low speed and heavy pull was very useful. It was to be retained at the site.

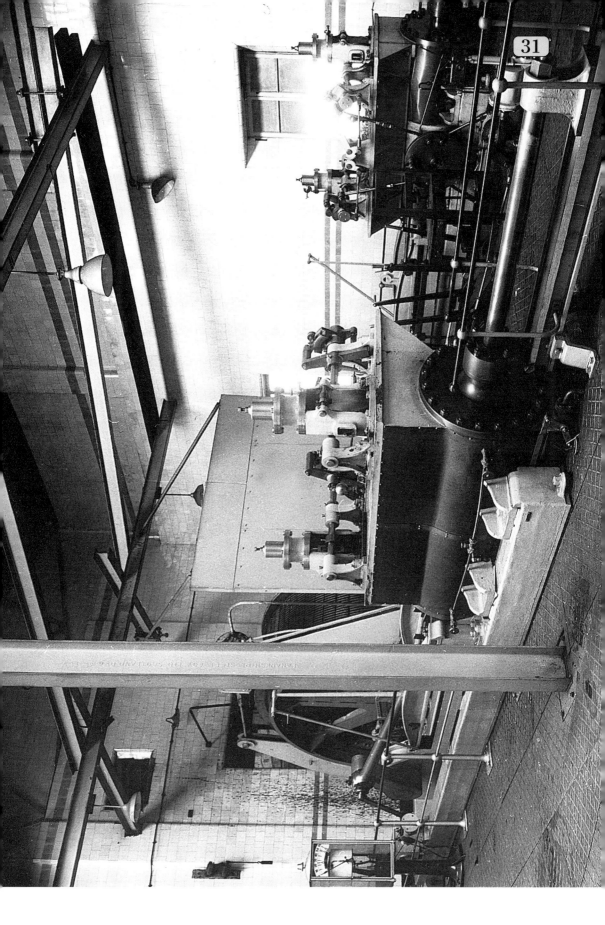

Perthshire

34 Blairgowrie, Thompson & Co., Keithbank Works   SER 1262a

Type:	High breast waterwheel
Photo taken:	1966
Maker and Date:	John Kerr & Co., Dundee, 1864
Cylinder/dimensions:	17ft 6in diameter x 13ft 0in wide
Hp: 75 ?	*Rpm:* 8 – 9 *Psi:* none
Service:	Mill drives by shafts, also oil engine

Thompson's were almost the last concern to run their waterwheels as regular parts of their power system, probably gaining well over 200 hp on average. They had the usual cast iron rims and arms, with similar iron rings between the bucket sections. The buckets were of timber, comprising flat boards set at an angle to each other, and close to the sole plate boards. They were ventilated by channels passing from one float to within about an inch of the next, with a channel about 8in wide to each of the three sections, made by the iron rings. The rim drive gearing was renewed in the 1950s by a foundry in Edinburgh. There was an Allen 100 hp oil engine coupled into the main driving shaft which drove alternators and some mechanical drives to the machines.

35 Blairgowrie, Thompson & Co., Keithbank Works   SER 1262b

Type:	Horizontal single cylinder condensing
Photo taken:	1966
Maker and Date:	Carmichael, Dundee ?, c. 1860
Cylinder/dimensions:	21in x 4ft 0in – drop inlet valves
Hp: 70	*Rpm:* 30 *Psi:* 75
Service:	Auxiliary drive – assisted water wheel

This was certainly mid-19th century but the cylinder was probably renewed by Carmichael of Dundee about 1900, but nothing certain was known of the history. The flywheel with round section rim was certainly really old, possibly from the 1840s. The drive was by mortise teeth held into the rim by circular pins in the tails. The engine was little used latterly since the oil engine assists the water power, but the steam engine came into use for some months when the oil engine failed in the 1960s. The mill was probably built about 1836, with water power only until this engine was installed. It is a neat piece of early Scottish engineering, well worth preserving.

36 Blairgowrie, Thompson & Co., Ashgrove Works   SER 1263a

Type:	High breast waterwheel
Photo taken:	1966
Maker and Date:	Thompson Bros., Dundee, 1871
Cylinder/dimensions:	19ft 0in x 22ft 0in wide
Hp: 180?	*Rpm:* 6.36 *Psi:* ?
Service:	Mill drive with 225hp Ruston oil engine by shafts and alternators

This was generally similar to the Keithbank wheel but was much wider. Owing to the width the wheel tended to twist around the axle with the torque, when driving from one side and a second spur gear ring was fitted at the other side of the wheel to counteract this by equalising the load at each end. This cured the trouble. The gear drive ring sectors of this were also renewed at the same time as those of the other wheel. The drives were efficient and economical powering the mill at low cost. The ventilation of the buckets was similar to that of the other wheel, i.e. a channel to each of the four sections.

35

37 Blairgowrie, Thompson & Co., Ashgrove Works — SER 1263b

Type:	Horizontal single cylinder condensing
Photo taken:	1966
Maker and Date:	Pierce Bros., Dundee, 1865
Cylinder/dimensions:	24ft x 3ft 0in – slide valve
Hp: 100 ?	*Rpm:* 50 *Psi:* 80
Service:	Auxiliary drive by gearing. Assist waterwheel

This ran for many years until the oil engine was installed, and possibly the variable cut-off valve on the inlet was an addition of the 1880s. It comprises a dropping valve tripped by the governor at variable points as the load demands. The engine is otherwise as built. It drove into the primary shaft of the waterwheel system, and so the slow speed required that it be geared down to the shaft, which revolved at one half of the engine speed, the drive being by cast iron herringbone toothed wheels. The Thompson mills were all in the flax trade, preparing, spinning and weaving it to fabric, but only Ashgrove and Keithbank used water power as the smaller ones had been abandoned.

38 Dunblane, Wilson & Sons, woollen mills — SER 1259

Type:	Horizontal cross compound condensing
Photo taken:	1966
Maker and Date:	Robey & Co., Lincoln, 1927
Cylinder/dimensions:	10in and 14in x 2ft 6in – drop valves
Hp: 170	*Rpm:* 120 *Psi:* 180
Service:	Woollen spinning. Shaft drives, later to alternator only

The mills always used water power and the last Gilkes' turbine developed 200 hp at 178 rpm. Originally the drives were by waterwheel and gearing, later assisted by a horizontal double cylinder engine geared into the mill mainshaft. The waterwheel was changed for a turbine about 1880, but the power system was long overloaded. It continued to run thus until the Robey engine was installed in 1927. This was arranged to allow the extraction of steam between the cylinders for wool washing etc. The drives were largely mechanical until the 1940s, and then electrical drives were installed, and a new water turbine was coupled to drive an alternator. The Robey engine was little used in later years, as with the increasing power demand, it was only just adequate. It was, however, a useful back-up, so long as the business was running.

39 Perth, Perth Waterworks Co., Tay Street Pumping Station — SER 1268

Type:	Inverted vertical triple expansion
Photo taken:	1966
Maker and Date:	Douglas & Grant, Kirkcaldy, 1904
Cylinder/dimensions:	27in, 18in, 42in x 2ft 0in – slide valves
Hp: 150	*Rpm:* 20 *Psi:* 120
Service:	Supply to town from River Tay. Surface lift only. Supply from beam engines from 1830

These later carried the main water supply load until 1930, when a Ruston oil engine and Worthington ram pumps were installed, and this was superseded by electrically driven Sulzer pumps in 1947. The load is now carried by an entirely new plant, away from the Tay Street site. Tay Street is interesting for the round engine house and fine matching chimney all in stone, which may remain, although the site is valuable and may have to be developed. The Douglas & Grant engines were interesting in that the high pressure cylinders were in the middle and had piston valves, whereas most waterworks sets were fitted with Corliss valves for economy. They were very plain and practical engines, with virtually nothing to go wrong and were regularly run for months on end, but oil engines had been on load so long that little real record of the steam sets was available. They pumped from the River Tay through settling tanks, by a ram pump beneath each crank connected by side rods to the crossheads.

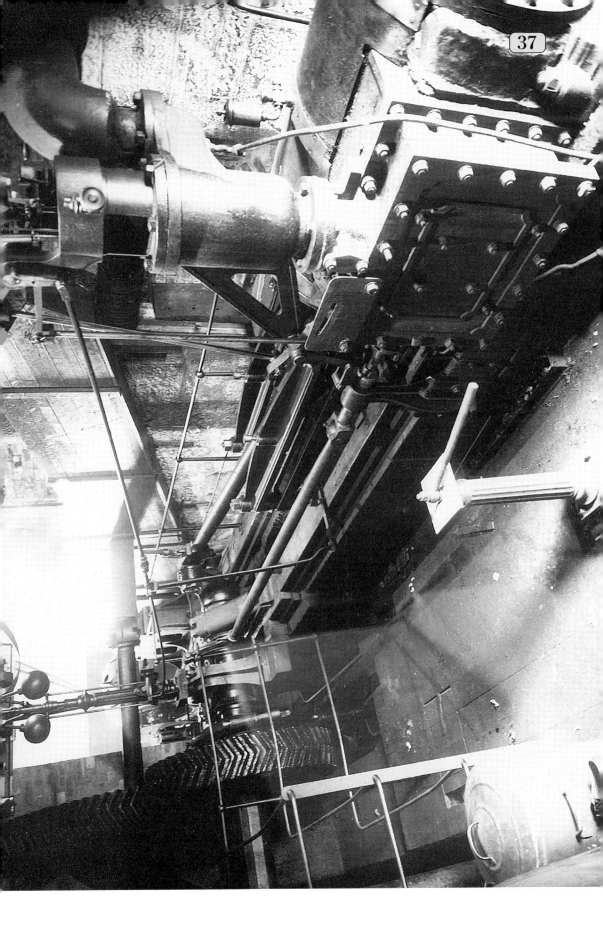

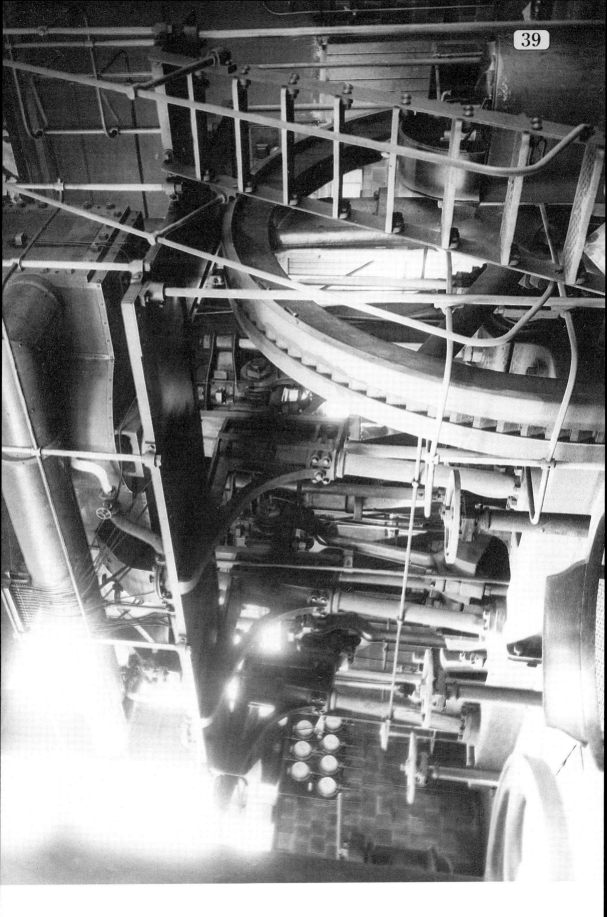

Roxburghshire

40 Hawick, W. Watson & Sons, Dangerfield Mills   SER 1046

Type:	Horizontal cross compound
Photo taken:	1961
Maker and Date:	J. Petrie & Co., Rochdale, 1874, altered later
Cylinder/dimensions:	Was 28in x 4ft 0in, then 18in and 27in x 4ft 0in
Hp: 250	*Rpm:* 75 *Psi:* 160
Service:	Woollen mill, drive by gears and shafts to four blocks

The business was started in 1780 on water power, and ran with this later assisted by a beam engine possibly of the 1840s, until 1873, when Petrie supplied a twin cylinder horizontal slide valve engine using steam at 30 psi. This ran so until 1910 when Petrie replaced the original with Corliss valve cylinders, with three boilers for 160 psi. Trouble later developed with Corliss valves, possibly due to superheat, and they were replaced with those seen in the photograph by Newton, Bean & Mitchell in 1924. These ran well, driving the whole with the waterwheel by extensive gearing to the weaving shed, both four and three floor blocks and a small section beside. The friction load was nearly 80 hp, and electrical driving was installed for the whole plant in 1961, when the old plant and shafting was removed.

41 Jedburgh, Laidlaw's, Allars blanket mills   SER 1048

Type:	Uniflow single
Photo taken:	1961
Maker and Date:	Douglas & Grant, Kirkcaldy, 1919
Cylinder/dimensions:	About 16in x 1ft 6in – drop valves
Hp: 200	*Rpm:* 130 *Psi:* 160
Service:	Woollen preparation and weaving

This worked in conjunction with the water wheel until the gearing of the water wheel drive was damaged by sand during a flood in 1959. The uniflow replaced two engines, and using 7 $\frac{1}{2}$ tons of coal per week was a great economy. It drove the weaving shed directly from the end of the crankshaft by an extension shaft across the yard, and the looms which were down the sides of the shed were driven by belts from the side shafts. This was probably the last of the small number of uniflow engines which Douglas & Grant built. The mill was closed and all scrapped in the early 1960s.

Selkirkshire

42 Galashiels, Kemp, Blair & Co., Textile Finishers   SER 1275

Type:	Horizontal single cylinder, non-condensing
Photo taken:	1966
Maker and Date:	Aimers, McLean, Galashiels, 1911
Cylinder/dimensions:	14in x 1ft 8in – slide valve
Hp: about 30	*Rpm:* 100 *Psi:* 80
Service:	Plant drive, 12in belt off 4ft 6in pulley

Aimers were the local engineers, and made many wall engines, as well as larger engines up to 300 hp. The designs were plain and practical, and, since most of the industry used process steam and hot water, were usually non-condensing, exhausting to heaters, as this one did. Kemp, Blair & Co., had also several Aimers, McLean wall engines once, but as machines were changed and motor driven units came in, these were superseded, and by 1968 only the horizontal remained, used as needed for part duties, and exhausting through a heater. It was 10ft long overall, and seemed likely to remain in use.

JEDWATER

DOUGLAS & GRANT Ltd
ENGINEERS, KIRKCALDY.
ENGINE No 704. 1919.

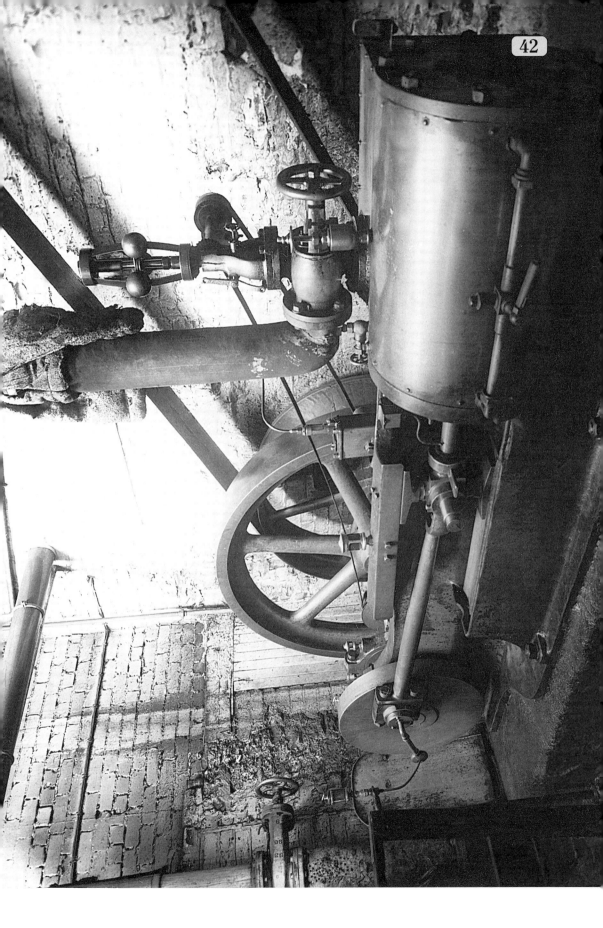

42

43 Selkirk, George Roberts & Co., Philiphaugh Mill   SER 1019

Type:	Horizontal twin tandem condensing
Photo taken:	1960
Maker and Date:	J Petrie & Co., Rochdale, 1911
Cylinder/dimensions:	12in and 24in x 2ft 6in – Corliss and piston valves
Hp: 450	*Rpm:* 100 *Psi:* 75
Service:	Woollen mill drive, combined with water turbines to one mill main shaft

This was an old water power site, once possibly with separate water wheels for the several buildings. The water power was later centralised into a large wheel, with a beam engine to assist this. The first water turbines were installed in 1878 when a new part was built on, and were replaced in 1920. The weaving shed was rebuilt or added in 1907, and possibly the Petrie engine was added soon after, as 1909 was mentioned as a replacement date for the beam engine, but the Petrie engine house was certainly dated 1911. The story was difficult to check, as there were certainly three engine rooms at the power end, suggesting one beam engine, and then a further one added later, and finally the Petrie engine in the latest house at the far end. The Petrie engine was at high level and directly connected to the second-motion shaft driven by the water turbines.

Stirlingshire

44 Alva, Glentana Mills   SER 1258

Type:	Horizontal single cylinder non – condensing
Photo taken:	1966
Maker and Date:	Douglas & Grant, Kirkcaldy, No 739, 1923
Hp: 80	*Rpm:* 90 *Psi:* 100
Service:	Mill drive. 10in belt off 8ft flywheel

This mill was similar to SER1257, with belt drives throughout, and exhausting to the works process heating system. It made fine cloth, ties and scarves, from woollen yarn, fully finished and packed for export and sale in Scotland as well as at the mill shop. The weaving shed was on the opposite side of the mill road to the engine, with a shaft across to it, there being a single pair of bevel wheels only, from the shaft across the yard to the shaft at the side of the shed. Most of the looms were made in Yorkshire by Hattersleys.

Cumberland

45 Cockermouth, Jennings & Co., The Castle Brewery   SER 1443

Type:	Horizontal direct with crank and flywheel
Photo taken:	1972
Maker and Date:	W.H. Bailey & Son, Salford, 1900s
Cylinder/dimensions:	About 6in x 9in – slide valve.
Hp: ?	*Rpm:* 20 *Psi:* 80
Service:	Plant pumps, hop backs to coolers

The plant was converted to all motor drives in 1960, but previously there was a Robey horizontal single cylinder engine which drove most of the plant by belts. It was about 9in x lft 0in plain slide valve. It was still in situ, and there was also a small vertical crank overhead engine in the older part, which it was hoped to preserve, but there is no record of its make or age. The small steam pumps were still used on brewing days, the Worthington (pump at the left of the photograph) more often than the Bailey, but it was still a useful standby. The steam and pump pistons were mounted upon one rod, with a single connecting rod from the crosshead to the crank pin.

43

45

46 Garside, nr Carlisle, The Mental Asylum   SER 612

Type:	Two compound Willans non-condensing, single acting
Photo taken:	1953
Maker and Date:	Willans & Robinson, c. 1906
Cylinder/dimensions:	No data available
Service:	Electricity and heat supply

These were in regular use in the 1950s, there being no outside electricity supply available then. Belliss and Morcom engines No 2042 and 5893 were added later but the Willans engines (Nos 3717/8) were fully used until outside current supply was available. All of the exhaust steam was passed through the heating and hot water service calorifiers, resulting in high economy. All was probably scrapped later.

47 Millom, Hodbarrow Iron Ore Mines   SER 554a

Type:	Cornish pump	
Photo taken:	1953	
Maker and Date:	Perran Foundry, Cornwall, 1878	
Cylinder/dimensions:	70in x 10ft 0in indoors and 9ft 0in for pumps	
Hp: no data	*Rpm:* no data	*Psi:* no data
Service:	Mine pump	

This was the last engine made by the Perran Foundry Co., and, intended for an Indian exhibition, was highly finished. It was supplied new to Millom, and ran until 1908 where originally erected, but was then moved since the original shaft was collapsing. This engine also ran until the mines were closed, but one of the three engines had fallen into the shaft in 1938, due to heavy mineral extraction around the base. In 1970 virtually nothing remained on the site at all.

48 Silloth, Carr's Flour Mill   SER 1249

Type:	Horizontal cross compound condensing	
Photo taken:	1966	
Maker and Date:	Carels, Frères, Ghent, 1904	
Cylinder/dimensions:	22 $\frac{1}{2}$ in and 37 $\frac{1}{2}$ in x 4ft 11in – drop valves	
Hp: 750	*Rpm:* 65	*Psi:* 160
Service:	Mill drive by 20 ropes off 18ft flywheel	

This engine (No 801) was purchased directly from the Paris Exhibition in 1903, and installed when the mill was built in 1904. It is an exceptional engine in all ways, having run at least six days per week for seventy years, and many times worked continuously for six weeks non-stop. It was always been well kept, and was kept in service as long as the senior partner, who was responsible for its installation, was in the business. It was in fact kept on for years after that into the 1970s. The slow speed is notable, as continental engines usually ran faster than English makes, and at work it is very dignified, quiet and steady. The condenser pumps were always separate from the engine, whereas Carels often drove the air pump from the engine crankpin, and the separate condenser is in the engine room. There was also a Pollit & wiggell tandem compound engine of 125 h.p. driving a provender section of the mills, but this was replaced by a motor in the 1960s. The Carel engine was certainly at work in 1973, although replacement was intended by 1970. The Babcock and Wilcox water tube boilers installed with the engine were also at work in 1973, still carrying the original working pressure. The steam is superheated to 150⁰C. The local farmers grew special wheat for the flour for making biscuits at the Carlisle mills.

49 Whitehaven, Haig Colliery, No 4 shaft   SER 1444

Type:	Double cylinder horizontal
Photo taken:	1972
Maker and Date:	Bever, Dorling, Bradford, 1914
Cylinder/dimensions:	30in x 5ft 0in – drop valves
Hp: ?	*Rpm:* 40 *Psi:* 120
Service:	Coal winding, 1 $\frac{1}{2}$ tons coal per wind, shaft 1100ft deep

No. 5 was the main drawing shaft until 1954, with the engine (with 40in x 7ft cylinders) fully loaded, winding up to 15,000 tons of coal per week, at 5 tons per wind. The two engines were identical in design, and in similar engine houses, with very little room around the larger engines. An unusual feature was that the backstays from the head gear were carried through the engine house wall directly to pads on the fronts of the engine beds, a logical but very rare design feature in horizontal engines. The piston tail rods were in tubular covers, with soft packed rear glands. There appeared to have been little alteration in the engines, which had been heavily used for some 60 years. This was the last steam wound colliery in the Cumberland area. These were probably the last Bever, Dorling engines left in U. K. There was an extensive set of mixed pressure turbine compressors and generators.

50 Workington, Workington Iron & Steel Co.   SER 1247

Type:	Double cylinder horizontal non-condensing
Photo taken:	1966
Maker and Date:	Davy Brothers, Sheffield, 1890s
Cylinder/dimensions:	32in x 4ft 0in – piston valves
Hp: 1700	*Rpm:* 70 *Psi:* 180
Service:	Steel rolling to flats 4in x $\frac{1}{4}$ in

The mill had three high rolls, with the metal passed through in each direction by hydraulic lifting tables, but the engine was a plain Davy Bros., reversing double cylinder which ran continuously, with the mill passing the metal over one and back through the lower set of rolls. It was bought second hand in 1912, possibly from Sheffield, and in 1954 new 32in cylinders to use up to 180 psi were fitted by Walkers of Wigan, replacing the original slide valve ones for 120 psi. It did exhaust into the works process steam system, at 25 psi back pressure, but latterly the exhaust was to the atmosphere. In 1966, it was rolling 2in thick down to 4in x $\frac{1}{4}$ in taking 100 seconds to complete this with 190 revolutions of the engine.

51 Workington, St Helens Colliery   SER 1248

Type:	Double cylinder horizontal
Photo taken:	1966
Maker and Date:	Milburn Engineering Co., Whitehaven (?), c.1890
Cylinder/dimensions:	28in x 4ft 6in – Cornish valves
Hp: ?	*Rpm:* 30 *Psi: ?*
Service:	Coal winding. Shaft 1000ft deep. 4 tubs = 44cwt per wind

This was almost certainly made locally, as there was a good engine-building tradition in the area, but there was nothing to suggest any maker. There were piston tail rods with ornate cast iron covers over the rods but no rear guides. Allan link motion was fitted and it was a simple engine, with nothing outstanding, but had certainly given very fine service, in working out the coal reserves. It was all to be scrapped on closing. There was a derelict steam fan, but electric drives had been installed for the fan and pumps many years before.

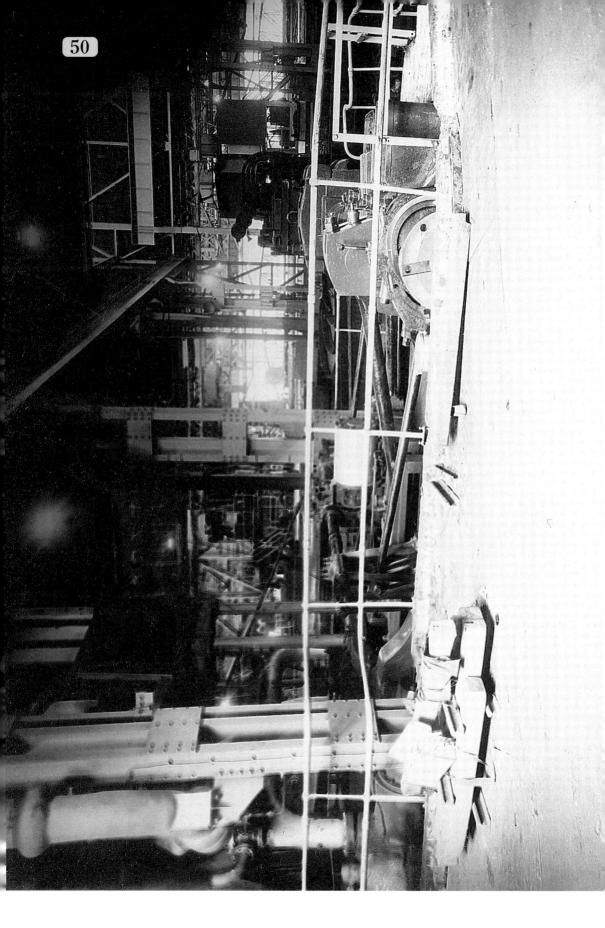

49

County Durham

52 Auckland Park, nr Bishop Auckland, Auckland Park Colliery SER 566

Type:	Stone engine house
Photo taken:	1953
Maker and Date:	Engine: T. Murray & Co., 1856, non-condensing
Cylinder/dimensions:	41ft x 6ft 6in – drop valves
Hp: ?	*Rpm:* 30 *Psi:* 60 – 80
Service:	Coal winding. Shaft 900ft deep about 1 $^3/_4$ tons of coal per wind

This was a typical Co. Durham vertical engine house, very solidly built of ashlar stone but the headgear for the pulleys was renewed in the 1920s; it was usually timber framed, and probably had rotted. The colliery was closed in the 1950s, but was retained as a pumping shaft afterwards. The engine had been fitted with a balance chain working in a staple pit beside the engine house, which had walls about 4ft thick.

53 Beamish, Beamish Colliery, Chop Hill Pit   SER 614

Type:	Vertical single cylinder – non-condensing
Photo taken:	1953
Maker and Date:	J & G Joicey, Newcastle-on-Tyne, No 20, 1855
Cylinder/dimensions:	About 24in x 5ft 0in
Hp: ?	*Rpm:* 40 *Psi:* 35
Service:	Coal winding

This was the last of the traditional timber framed Co. Durham vertical engines in use, and was retained to work out the small amount of high class coal remaining in the seams. The output of 800 tons per week from 380 feet deep was always sold ahead. The engine was usually worked by the hand valve gear levers; it was only 6 $^1/_2$ revolutions per wind in the later years when only winding from 180 feet deep. There were 6 boilers at the pit; one only regularly steamed the vertical engine, but three were necessary earlier when there was a haulage from the nearby drift pit.

54 Beamish, Beamish Colliery, Chop Hill Pit   SER 614a

Type:	Valve gear
Photo taken:	1953
Maker and Date:	J & G Joicey, Newcastle-on-Tyne, 1855
Cylinder/dimensions:	No other data
Hp:	*Rpm:* *Psi:*
Service:	Coal winding

This was unaltered from the date of construction, except for the addition of a mechanical lubricator, and the several depth indicators. It retained the old style-cone and bridle valve spindle packing system, and the neatly swept supporting brackets for the valve gear arbors were attractive. It had given very good and hard worked service for over a century when it ceased work.

54

55 Beamish, Beamish Colliery, Mary Pit   SER 615

Type: Vertical single cylinder non-condensing
Photo taken: 1953
Maker and Date: J & G Joicey, Newcastle-on-Tyne, Works No 380, 1887
Cylinder/dimensions: 45in x 6ft 0in – drop valves
Hp: 250?   *Rpm: 36*   *Psi: 40*
Service: Coal winding. Shaft 836ft deep. 2 tons of coal per wind

Although containing many refinements over No.20 at Chop Hill, the broad outline of the Co. Durham vertical engine had not changed. The framing was now, however, a mixture of cast and wrought iron members, and the parallel motion beams were of steel plate. The very neat brackets for and arbors upon the valve gear remained. The wooden lagging on the cylinder and the neat valve chest castings made the engine as a whole one of the best of its type. It was scrapped when the electric winders came into action in 1953.

56 Bearpark, Bearpark Colliery   SER 374

No data on the SER card.

57 Bearpark, Bearpark Colliery   SER 374a

Type: Vertical single cylinder condensing
Photo taken: 1951
Maker and Date: J & G Joicey, Newcastle-on-Tyne, 1874
Cylinder/dimensions: 60in x 7ft 6in – drop valves
Hp: 500   *Rpm: 19 – 20*   *Psi: 30 – 35*
Service: Coal winding shaft 484ft deep, round rope drum
                          17ft 6in diameter

This was in regular use, virtually unaltered until 1958, pulling a full load of 100 score of trucks of 12 cwt of coal daily. The framework supporting the crankshaft bearing was a mixture of cast and wrought iron members, with forged plate parallel motion beams, 16ft 0in long. Plain forged crank and connecting rod, but neat square pattern valve gear arbor shaft-brackets.

58 Bearpark, Bearpark Colliery   SER 374b

Type:	Engine house and headgear of 374a
	Engine house 65ft 0in high x 30ft 0in
Photo taken:	1951

Fine brick engine house typical of the later period of Co. Durham, but with unusual headgear layout. The pulley frames were of timber, but the backstays to the engine house, usually sharply inclined were here nearly horizontal to the pulleys. The fitting of a second set below these was also uncommon in Co. Durham.

59 Burnhope, Burnhope Colliery   SER 515

Type:	Horizontal single cylinder non-condensing	
Photo taken:	1952	
Maker and Date:	J & G Joicey, Newcastle-on-Tyne, 1868	
Cylinder/dimensions:	36in x 5ft 3in – drop valves	
Hp: ?	*Rpm:* 25	*Psi:* 50
Service:	Coal winding 600ft deep	

This engine was really a bridge between the traditional Co. Durham vertical single cylinder, and the twin cylinder which was to become the standard type for winding for a century. The flywheel acting as a brake track, and the small drum were features of the older type, but overwinding and slow banking units had been fitted later, and also a governor-controlled steam cut-off gear, which was highly economical. These however were the only alterations in some 80 years of heavy work. The colliery was closed in 1950, but possibly the reserves of coal below the worked-out section would be won from another pit. All was scrapped in the early 1950s.

60 Burnhope, Burnhope Colliery, Fortune Pit   SER 375a

Type:	Vertical single cylinder non-condensing	
Photo taken:	1951	
Maker and Date:	T. Murray & Co., Chester-le-Street, c. 1844	
Cylinder/dimensions:	27in x 5ft 0in – drop valves	
Hp: 50 – 60	*Rpm:* 28	*Psi:* 50
Service:	Coal winding No 1 shaft 20 tons per hour 420ft 0in deep	

Last remaining engine in the county with the pumping beam incorporated in the parallel motion. This was 20ft 0in long, i.e. double the length of the other one, and projected through the engine house wall, and drove the pumps by a similar beam at ground level to the rods in the shaft. This was probably used to pump as the shaft was sunk. Almost unaltered, the main *A* framing consisted of pine timbers 15in square, supporting the crankshaft bearing. The neat boss in the middle of the connecting rod, cast iron parallel motion beams with jaw ends, end tee section flywheel arms were unaltered in a century of work.

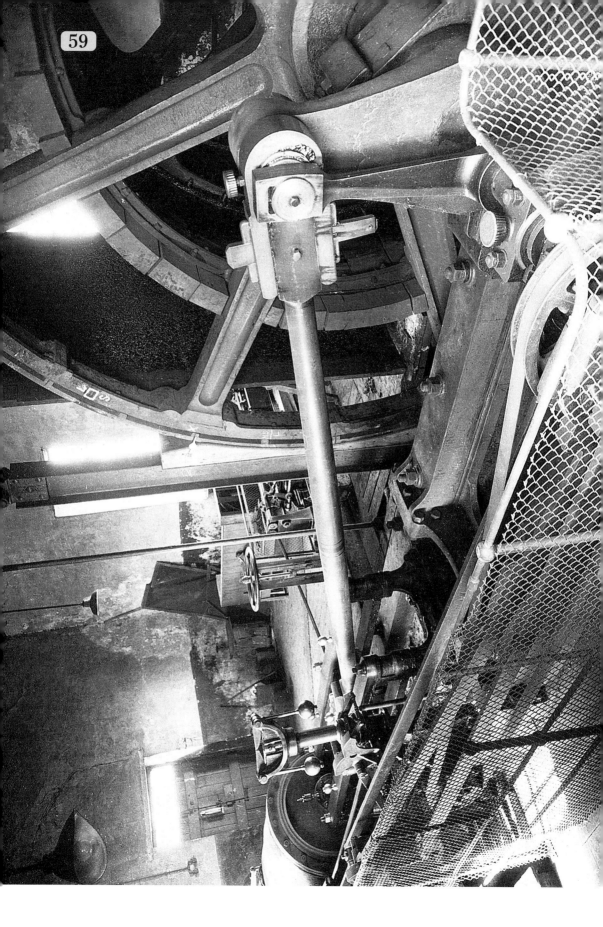

61 Burnhope, Burnhope Colliery, Fortune Pit   SER 375b

Type:	Cylinder & valve gear
Photo taken:	1951
Maker and Date:	
Cylinder/dimensions:	
Hp: *Rpm:* *Psi:*	
Service:	

These too were typical and unaltered, with very neat forged bosses on the rod end eyes and hand levers. The foot brake was in use to the end, but in later years a King's slow banker and Worth McKenzie overwinder were fitted. No joint was visible in the top and bottom valve chest and side pipes, an assembly nearly 7ft 0in high. It is possible that the whole was, in fact, a single casting.

62 Burnhope, Burnhope Colliery, Fortune Pit   SER 375c

Type:	Stone engine house 1844?
Photo taken:	1951
Maker and Date:	
Cylinder/dimensions:	
Hp: *Rpm:* *Psi:*	
Service:	

This was about 30ft 0in high, and 20ft 0in square. The wooden headgear and heavy timber raking backstays to the engine house were unaltered and typical of the early but sound construction of the period. The pumping beam can be seen projecting through the engine house wall slot, many of the early engines being designed thus, to pump out as the pit was sunk. The brick structure around the pithead was much later, the pit tops or banks usually being open, or very lightly cased. The winding drum was always fitted to the crankshaft in these engines, and the bricked aperture seen in the upper part of the side wall was provided to allow the rapid removal of the crankshaft if this was ever necessary.

63 Burnhope, Burnhope Colliery, Fortune Pit   SER 378

Type:	Combined beam and horizontal non-condensing
Photo taken:	1951
Maker and Date:	Beam engine: T. Murray & Co., Chester le Street 1845; Horizontal ? 1860-70
Cylinder/dimensions:	Beam 24in x 5ft 0in – slide valve Horizontal 24in x 5ft 0in – slide valve
Hp: ? *Rpm:* 20 *Psi:* 40	
Service:	Bank haulage for trucks over incline to River Tyne

Drove two winding drums by a single pinion on the crankshaft, the winding drums being arranged to slide so that either could be engaged with the engine pinion. The beam engine had been overloaded, having fractures in the cylinder and beam, the horizontal engine probably being installed to assist it. Both engines drove the same crankpin and shaft, the horizontal crankpin bearing being split into a jaw on either side of that of the beam engine. There was only one set of controls for the two engines.

64 Chilton, Chilton Colliery   SER 567

Type:	Vertical twin cylinder non-condensing
Photo taken:	1953
Maker and Date:	Andrew Barclay & Co., Kilmarnock?, 1876
Cylinder/dimensions:	42in x 6ft 0in – drop valves
Hp: 450	*Rpm:* 30 *Psi:* 80
Service:	Coal winding. Rope drum 16ft diameter

These were built for steam at 60 psi, and latterly worked at 80-100 psi. Plain Stephenson link reversing gear was fitted, and the steam cut-off control was still connected. The colliery was due to be converted to electric winding in the 1960s, but many pits were closed instead and Chilton was only a pumping shaft in 1970.

65 Craghead, nr Stanley, Oswald Colliery   SER 613

Type:	Single cylinder non-condensing beam
Photo taken:	1953
Maker and Date:	Dunston Engineering Co., Durham, 1897
Cylinder/dimensions:	32in x 6ft 0in – piston valve
Hp: ?	*Rpm:* 30 *Psi:* 60
Service:	Coal winding. Shaft 468ft deep

This was the last to remain of four similar engines made by Dunston Engineering in the 1890s, which were almost certainly the last beam winding engines to be built. The design was largely of cast iron, except for the entablature and longitudinal girders and the beam flitches. The winding rope drum was directly connected to the flywheel arms, which with the use of the flywheel rim as a brake track were unusual because of the latter's cast iron construction. It was reversed by a slipping eccentric, the valve being hand-operated to start the engine in the required direction. The colliery was closed in the later reorganisations and all was scrapped.

66 Dalton, nr Seaham, Sunderland Waterworks,
Dalton Pumping Station   SER 372

Type:	Two Cornish beam engines
Photo taken:	1951
Maker and Date:	Davy Brothers, Sheffield, 1879
Cylinder/dimensions:	72in x 9ft 0in
Hp:	*Rpm:* 6 – 8 *Psi:* 40
Service:	Town water from well. One bucket pump off end of beam, 919,000 gallons per day from each engine

This was interesting in being almost the only Cornish cycle engine to work with superheat, ie up to 165^{0}C steam temperature. The fuel used was about 6 tons per day for one engine. The whole plant was typical of Hawksley's practice with the massive square chimney with gallery around it, but the electric pumps were installed in the 1930s, although the engines were used later at times. There were four Lancashire boilers. It is likely that the makers made few other Cornish engines.

67 Darlington, Darlington Waterworks, Coniscliffe Road, Pumping Station   SER 513

Type:	One Woolf compound beam
Photo taken:	1952
Maker and Date:	Teasdale Bros, Darlington, 1904
Cylinder/dimensions:	About 18in x 5ft 6in & 29in x 7ft 0in – drop valves
Hp: 100	*Rpm:* 10 - 12 *Psi:* 100
Service:	Town supply from river 2 $^1/_2$ – 3 million gallons per day

Water supply was always from the River Tees, by 2 sets of pumps, the low lift transferring to the settling reservoirs, and the high lift thence to service reservoirs; the total head was about 200ft. The first supply was in 1849, with beam engines, which served to 1904, and later suction gas engines with belt drive to ram pumps replaced the Teasdale engine. Electric pumps were then installed possibly in the 1920s, but the Teasdale Bros. engine was used as standby for many years afterwards. The site was typical of T. & C. Hawksley's practice.

68 Darlington, Darlington Waterworks, Coniscliffe Road, Pumping Station   SER 1496

Type:	Suction gas engines and three throw pumps
Photo taken:	1975
Maker and Date:	Ruston Hornby? 1920
Cylinder/dimensions:	Sizes unknown
Hp: about 200	*Rpm:* 200 *Psi:* ?
Service:	Town water supply from shallow well

This plant was installed to deal with increasing demand, which the beam engine (SER 513) could not meet. It is typical of the economical internal combustion engines that were developed, and consisted of a twin gas producer making gas from anthracite coal which although more expensive gave far less trouble than tarry house coal did (however well the gas was scrubbed). The twin gas engine drove by a wide belt to a countershaft and gearing to either set of three throw pumps, allowing pumping to continue during overhauls of pumps. The load had long been taken by electric pumps, and although intact and workable it was doubtful if staff who could run the gas producers was available.

69 Darlington, Tees Valley Water Board, Broken Scar Pumping Station   SER 1017

Type:	Two single beam Woolf compound
Photo taken:	1960
Maker and Date:	W & J Yates, Canal Foundry, Blackburn, 1886
Cylinder/dimensions:	20in x 5ft 0in and 30in x 7ft – slide shaft
Hp: each about 120	*Rpm:* 16 *Psi:* 120
Service:	Town supply from well. One pump to each?

There was little record available of this plant, as it had long been disused, but there was a single well pump at the crank end of the beam, which may have pumped only into the reservoir at the station. An unusual feature for a waterworks engine was the Varley type of cross cut-off slide valve driven from a vertical shaft at the side of the high pressure cylinder. There may also have been a pump driven from a tail rod under the high pressure cylinder, to lift the water to high level. The engines had heavy usage over the years, but needed little attention. There were other pumps at the station but all of the steam plant was cleared by the mid-1960s following a major reconstruction of the system.

70 Easington, Eppleton Colliery   SER 376a

Type:	Two non-condensing vertical single cylinder
Photo taken:	1957
Maker and Date:	*Jane*: T. Murray & Co., c. 1826, rebuilt J & G Joicey, 1829 (new cylinder 1872)
	Caroline: J & G Joicey, Newcastle-on-Tyne, 1872
Cylinder/dimensions:	*Jane* 40in x 6ft 0in *Caroline* 36in x 6ft 0in
Hp:	*Rpm:* 18 *Psi:* 35
Service:	Coal winding with round ropes

Two engines in a single house were rare in Co. Durham. The engine at the left was *Jane*, which had been superseded by another engine and headgear, although possibly maintained as usable until scrapped in 1950. It is probable that *Jane* had had a new winding drum, since the earlier ones often had tee section arms. *Caroline* was in regular use later, until electrification in 1958.

71 Easington, Eppleton Colliery   SER 376b

Type:	Vertical engine 'Caroline'
Photo taken:	1951
Maker and Date:	J & G Joicey, Newcastle-upon-Tyne, 1872
Cylinder/dimensions:	36in x 6ft 0in – drop valves
Hp: 180	*Rpm:* 18 – 20 *Psi:* 35
Service:	Coal winding shaft 888ft deep

Typical of Joicey's late design, with glands instead of the old cone and bridle type of valve arbor shafts, and separate side pipes bolted to the valve chests by flanges. Unaltered in 75 years of work, the wear upon the hand operating levers of the valve gear suggests that the valves were largely worked by hand throughout the stroke as many engine men preferred to do. This was due to the large rope drums, which, in a shallow, shaft, made as little as 14 revolutions per wind, and always had to be started and stopped by hand.

72 Easington, Eppleton Colliery   SER 376c

Type:	Brick engine house c1880
Photo taken:	1951
Maker and Date:	
Cylinder/dimensions:	
Hp:	*Rpm:* *Psi:*
Service:	Coal winding

Since this was built several years after the second of the two engines, it suggests that *Caroline*, the later one, was in temporary housing until then. The house was about 40ft 0in long, 40ft 0in high x 20ft 0in wide, with a staple pit for the counterbalance chains at one side, beneath the chain drums seen on the ends of the crankshafts. *Caroline* at the left of the photograph retained the counter balance chain in use to the end, and it can be seen sloping at an angle to the staple pit beneath the drum of *Jane's* drum. *Jane* had twin exhaust pipes but *Caroline* a single large one.

73 Elemore, nr Easington, Elemore Colliery   SER 565a

Type:	Vertical single cylinder non-condensing
Photo taken:	1953
Maker and Date:	Uncertain, c. 1820s, shaft sunk 1825
Cylinder/dimensions:	39in x 6ft 0in – drop valves
Hp: ?	*Rpm:* 30 *Psi:* 35
Service:	Coal winding 600ft deep. 27cwt coal per wind

This was possibly a Murray engine and retained the massive timber *A* framing 24in by 12in section until electric winding was installed in the late 1950's. It was a valuable engine, and when the heavy demand arose for coal in 1950, the crankshaft broke and having a spare one on hand, it was replaced and the engine was running again in under 30 hours. The three deck cage was a disadvantage (i.e. 3 landings per wind), but its fast speed offset this. It had certainly been rebuilt, also a new cylinder was fitted in 1938, and it was said of the old one that it was very difficult to break up. There was a counterbalance chain on an outside drum, working into a staple pit. The other engine was a Davy Bros., Sheffield, twin engine of 1870, also a vertical engine bought second hand from Yorkshire about 1908.

74 Elemore, nr Easington, Elemore Colliery   SER 565b

Type:	Twin cylinder non-condensing
Photo taken:	1953
Maker and Date:	Davy Brothers, Sheffield, 1870s
Cylinder/dimensions:	42in x 5ft 0in – drop valves
Hp: 400	*Rpm:* ?30 *Psi:* 50
Service:	Colliery winding, shaft 600ft deep 35cwt coal per wind

This probably came from a Yorkshire colliery about 1908, and latterly was the main coal winding engine for the colliery. It was a typical Yorkshire engine with link motion reversing gear whereas the typical Co. Durham engine was hand reversed, with the valves driven from a plug rod from the parallel motion guiding system of the crosshead. The substantial cast iron *A* frames were also Yorkshire, rather than Co. Durham practice. The winding drum was supported by massive stone walls between the two cylinders.

75 Ferryhill, Dean and Chapter Colliery   SER 568

Type:	Inverted vertical – Corliss valve compound
Photo taken:	1953
Maker and Date:	Walker Brothers, Pagefield Works, Wigan, No 10572
Cylinder/dimensions:	18in & 32in x 3ft 0in – Corliss valves
Hp: about 350	*Rpm:* 70 *Psi:* 120
Service:	Ventilating fan drive about 16 ropes to drive fan

Most of Walker's fan engines were horizontal, and no reason was known for this being vertical. It was certainly a stiff and well made engine, with forged steel cross stays low on the columns, and a solid entablature at the top across the them. Counterbalance weights were fitted to the cranks, and no condenser was fitted to the engine. The pit was closed in the 1960s.

76 Hetton, South Hetton Colliery   *SER 370a*

Type:	Vertical single cylinder condensing
Photo taken:	1951
Maker and Date:	T. Richardson, Hartlepool, 1851
Cylinder/dimensions:	45in x 6ft 0in-drop valves
Hp: 300	*Rpm:* 20 *Psi:* 28
Service:	Coal winding shaft 840ft deep round ropes replaced by electric set 1956

A late example of the early Co. Durham design, in which the crankshaft bearing was supported by a massive timber "A" frame, in this case of double 12in x 12in timbers. The flywheel was 27ft 6in diameter, and the drum 23ft 0in, making the wind in l3 $^1/_2$ revolutions. It was fitted with a counterbalance chain drum on the end of the crankshaft, outside the house but, with the main load later taken by a horizontal engine, which was disused. It was one of the very few Co. Durham engines of the type to be worked expansively. (See SER 370c).

77 Hetton, South Hetton Colliery   *SER 370b*

Type:	Valve chest of vertical engine
Photo taken:	1951
Maker and Date:	
Cylinder/dimensions:	
Hp:	*Rpm:* *Psi:*
Service:	Coal winding shaft 840ft deep round ropes replaced by electric set 1956

Taken when the engine was broken up, the print shows the original valve chest of 1851, with the valves driven by a sector and rack from the arbor shaft. The air pump and plug rod has been cut off and is seen inclined across the engine front. The socket and spigot joints in the side steam and exhaust pipes were usually caulked with rusted iron borings. The upper valve seen is the top exhaust valve, the inlet valve being above this. The massive and intricate castings were typical of the craftmanship of the early Victorian period.

78 Hetton, South Hetton Colliery   *SER 370c*

Type:	Worth McKenzie expansion gear
Photo taken:	1951
Maker and Date:	
Cylinder/dimensions:	
Hp:	*Rpm:* *Psi:*
Service:	Coal winding shaft 840ft deep round ropes replaced by electric set 1956. Vary the steam admission during winding

The Durham vertical engines did not usually work expansively and the valves were often hand operated all of the time. The Worth McKenzie gear consisted of a pair of side plates, which made one revolution per wind, with cam tracks cut in the faces, one for each direction. The valves were driven by a vertical hanging lever with pins to engage in the tracks, the lever being slid from one track to the other to reverse the engine. Since the cut-off varied for each stroke, the cam track had to do the same, so that each gear was individual to the shaft and conditions. There was also an inner track on each face for the exhaust valves, which had constant movement.

79 New Herrington, New Herrington Colliery   SER 564

Type:	Vertical single cylinder condensing
Photo taken:	1953
Maker and Date:	T. Murray & Co., Chester-le-Street c 1874
Cylinder/dimensions:	56in x 7ft 0in – drop valves
Hp: ?	*Rpm:* 18 *Psi:* 35
Service:	Coal winding 51cwt per wind

This was the last engine to be made by Murray (established in the 1830s) before they closed in 1874. It was quite large with framing of wrought and cast iron, which carried the 20ft diameter drum for the circular winding rope at 30ft above the engine room floor. It retained several of the sound traditional features, i.e. parallel motion guiding, counterbalance weight in the flywheel rim, heavy flywheel, but was practical in that some of the earlier decorative features were omitted. It did retain the pineapples cast upon the top of the very neat valve gear support framing, whilst the provision of a gallery packing platform was unusual in Co. Durham vertical engines. Electric winding was installed in the 1950s.

80 Ryhope, Sunderland Waterworks Ryhope Pumping Station SER 371a

Type:	2 Woolf compound beam
Photo taken:	1951
Maker and Date:	R & W Hawthorn, Newcastle-on-Tyne, 1868
Cylinder/dimensions:	27in x 5ft 4in and 45in x 8ft 0 in – drop valves
Hp: 60 each	*Rpm:* 8 – 10 *Psi:* 40
Service:	Town water supply from wells. One million gallons per day each, 240ft lift

The pair of engines were quite separate, but unusual in that although lifting only from the wells, there were two sets of pumps to each engine, each lifting the water half way. The pumps were placed at the end of the beams, with l0ft 0in stroke, since they overhung the cylinders and the crankshaft which had an 8ft 0in stroke. The set at the flywheel end lifted to 120ft down, the set near the cylinder lifted to the surface, i.e. 120ft each. The flywheels are 24ft 0in diameter. Electric pumps were installed in the 1960s. Engines were preserved in situ.

81 Ryhope, Sunderland Waterworks Ryhope Pumping Station SER 371b

Type:	Parallel motion of the steam end
Photo taken:	1951
Maker and Date:	R & W Hawthorn, Newcastle-on-Tyne, 1868
Cylinder/dimensions:	27in x 5ft 4in and 45in x 8ft 0 in – drop valves
Hp: 60 each	*Rpm:* 8 – 10 *Psi:* 40
Service:	Town water supply from wells. One million gallons per day each, 240ft lift

The engines were virtually unaltered in some 90 years use, except that following the breakage of one cast iron connecting rod, both were replaced by steel. The cylinders were connected to the beam by the usual parallel motion, but not at the end of the beam, and the photograph shows how the pump rods were connected to the extreme end, thus having a longer stroke than the cranks, ie l0ft 0in for the pumps.

82 Sherburn, Sherburn Hill Colliery, East Pit   SER 377a

Type:	Vertical single cylinder non-condensing
Photo taken:	1951
Maker and Date:	T. Murray & Co., Chester-le-Street, 1868
Cylinder/dimensions:	36in x 5ft 6in – drop valves
Hp:	*Rpm:* 18 - 20 *Psi:* 40
Service:	Coal winding to Busty seam 225ft 0in deep

The east shaft was sunk in 1835, and the west in 1837, and latterly there were three engines similar to this at the pit, possibly dating from the sinking of the third shaft. The acorn decorations on the arbor shaft posts was unusual in Co. Durham. This was the last of the three and was unsafe from failing foundations in 1954. Again typical late Murray design, the parallel motion beams were forged but the rest of the engine was mainly of cast iron. It was dismantled in 1955.

83 Sherburn, Sherburn Hill Colliery, East Pit   SER 377b

Type:	Stone engine house 1868, about 30ft 0in high x 20ft 0in x 30ft 0in area
Photo taken:	1951
Maker and Date:	
Cylinder/dimensions:	
Hp:	*Rpm:* *Psi:*
Service:	Coal winding to Busty seam 225ft deep

This had had a counterbalance chain on the outside drum working in the usual staple pit. The headgear was largely of wrought iron, with the single upright members and massive backstays frequently met in Co. Durham. It gave little trouble in 80 years of heavy work until the foundations failed and it had to be dismantled.

84 Staindrop, nr Barnard Castle, Maudes, Clog Soles   SER 1277a

Type:	Double cylinder horizontal, non-condensing
Photo taken:	1966
Maker and Date:	Tangye Ltd., Birmingham, 1890s
Cylinder/dimensions:	12in and 12in x 1ft 9in – slide valves
Hp: 50	*Rpm:* 120 *Psi:* 120
Service:	Sawmill drive, 12in belt off 8ft 0in flywheel

A standard Tangye engine with plain slide valves, trunk frames, and cast iron disc cranks this frequently carried considerable overloads at times. The timber was received from the fellers in the rough, and the machinery worked this down to rough formed clog soles, which then went to Hebden Bridge, Yorkshire for finishing. The mill was driven by an underground shaft, from which a second shaft was also driven and to the numerous machines by belts up through the floor. This made it easy to handle long timber safely with no risk of contact with overhead belting, and shafts. There was an exhaust steam feed water heater, but otherwise the plant was as simple as possible, which was desirable in view of its isolated situation.

85 Staindrop, nr Barnard Castle, Maudes, clog soles   SER 1277b

Type:	Horizontal colonial type boiler
Photo taken:	1966
Maker and Date:	Tangye Ltd., Birmingham, 1890s
Cylinder/dimensions:	14ft 6in long x 5ft 0in diameter
Hp: 50	*Rpm:* ? *Psi:* 120
Service:	Steam raising for plant

This was the plain drum with return tubes through the shell to the chimney. There were 66 tubes of 2 $\frac{1}{2}$ in diameter x 13ft long, the drum being supported upon the brick setting by 4 steel lugs on each side. The smokebox and chimney were at the front above the firing door, access for sweeping the tubes being through the swinging door above the fire door. Since the smokebox was at the end, the fittings usually located there were placed at the side of the drum. Throughout, the little plant was as simple as possible, and since the large firebox allowed waste wood to be burned, it was also quite economical; coal would have had to be hauled over a considerable distance. It gave some 65 years service, making roughed-out clog soles as long as the trade lasted, but latterly the demand fell off, and the little mill was dismantled and the site completely cleared in 1972.

86 Sunderland, Monkwearmouth Colliery   SER 369a

Type:	Vertical single cylinder condensing
Photo taken:	1951
Maker and Date:	*A* pit: T. Murray & Co., 1849, rebuilt by Joicey 1866
	B pit: Joicey 1868
Cylinder/dimensions:	A: 61in x 7ft 0in
	B: 65in x 7ft 0in
Hp: 600	*Rpm:* 18 *Psi:* 35
Service:	Coal winding *A* and *B* pits. 1800 feet deep

Two typical. Co. Durham vertical low pressure engines. There were two cages in each shaft, winding with flat steel ropes. Each was fitted with chain counterbalance (see SER 369c), and the print is interesting in showing the pulleys of the *A* engine above each other, while those of the later *B* engine are side by side.

87 Sunderland, Monkwearmouth Colliery   SER 369b

Type:	Engine house and headgears
Photo taken:	1951
Maker and Date:	Murray, Chester-le-Street
Cylinder/dimensions:	61in x 7ft 0in
Hp: 600	*Rpm:* 18 *Psi:* 35
Service:	*A* engine coal winding

The Durham vertical engine at its best, this later worked with a higher steam pressure and carried a full load when a century old. The counterbalance system is at the left, where the heavy chain bunches counterweights are seen above the pit top. The girder structure was neat and strong, almost all of wrought iron and largely blacksmith made. The stone house was nearly 60ft high, and about 40ft 0in by 30ft 0in in area, and in a century had needed little attention.

88 Sunderland, Monkwearmouth Colliery   SER 369c

Type: Winding reels 20ft 0in minimum diameter
                         counterbalance 8ft 0in diameter
Service: A engine winding and counterbalance rope reels

The Durham single cylinder engines were too heavily loaded to start the load away
from the bottom unaided, so they were provided with counterbalance systems
which by chain masses aided the engine for the first half of the wind and checked it
for the latter part. The winding rope on the larger reel had to work in the same
direction for the whole wind, but the counterbalance wound on to the smaller
drum, which, paying off the first half of the wind, rewound upon the drum for the
second half. It thus aided the engine whilst unwinding, i.e. until the cages met at
mid wind, when all of the counterbalance chain was wound off the smaller reel at
the right and then wound back again, retarding the engine, as the cage came to the
top.

89 Sunderland, Monkwearmouth Colliery   SER 563

Type: Horizontal double cylinder
Photo taken: 1953
Maker and Date: Bever, Dorling & Co., Bradford, 1880
Cylinder/dimensions: 34in x 5ft 9in – drop valves
Hp: no data   *Rpm:* no data   *Psi:* no data
Service: Coal winding shaft 840ft deep, parallel drum 24ft diameter

The C shaft was sunk in the 1880s to work other coal than the early (1830/40s)
two shafts (see SER 369), and latterly exhausted into a low pressure turbine, until
the re-organisation of the pits. Then one old and C shafts were fitted with tower
electric winders. It was a massive engine which did not appear to have been altered
except for overwind and banking controls, even retaining the soft packed glands,
whereas many engines were fitted with metallic packings later. It was one of Bever,
Dorling's larger engines and heavily built. All steam had gone by 1965.

90 Thornley, nr Durham, Thornley Colliery   SER 1298a

Type: Double cylinder horizontal
Photo taken: 1967
Maker and Date: Varley & Yeadon, Leeds, 1880s
Cylinder/dimensions: 42in x 6ft 0in – Cornish valves
Hp: ?   *Rpm:* 35   *Psi:* 60
Service: Coal winding, shaft 1050ft deep, drum 16ft 6in diameter

This was the original winding engine at the pit and had been very heavily used, and
it is probable the first engine at the other shaft was similar. The valve chests with
their large volume must have been wasteful, but the engine handled well, with light
controls. This was massive with deep beds, but the repair straps around the ends of
the rear ends of the beds suggests that this engine, too, had suffered from subsidence and heavy work; generally it was almost unaltered except for the repairs and
the additional safety details required by law. The engineman's driving platform was
above the engine room floor, an arrangement that allowed him to watch the land-
ing of the cage; most engines were driven from the floor level, but the high level of
the window sills interfered. An interesting design feature was that the lower guide
surface for the crosshead was cast in one with the engine bed; it was not separate
and bolted on as usual.

91 Thornley, nr Durham, Thornley Colliery — SER 1298b

Type:	Double cylinder horizontal
Photo taken:	1967
Maker and Date:	A Barclay & Co., Kilmarnock, early 1900s
Cylinder/dimensions:	32in x 5ft 0in – Corliss valves
Hp: ?	*Rpm:* 45 *Psi:* 120
Service:	Coal winding, shaft 1050ft deep, drum 16ft diameter, 4 tons per wind

There was a good deal of modernising of an old colliery which had nearly worked out the coal and was to be closed in the late 1960s. The No 1 engine was the original, but the No 2 had certainly been replaced, and was the main engine in use later. It had very heavy use and the trip gear for the Corliss valves was removed, as it was considered to be damaging to the engine. The cylinders were rebored in 1932, and tail pistons rods were then added, and the new bed plates were fitted in 1936. A new slow banker was fitted 1939, and a new crank in 1952 replaced a damaged one. A further re-bore followed in 1955, and the beds were lifted and re-aligned in 1961, and a new right hand cylinder was also fitted at some time. All of this suggests heavy usage, and subsidence around the colliery. It was to be closed in 1969, when all would be scrapped.

92 Warden Law, National Coal Board Colliery — SER 373

Type:	Single cylinder non-condensing beam
Photo taken:	1951
Maker and Date:	T. Murray & Co., Chester-le-Street, 1836
Cylinder/dimensions:	39in x 6ft 6in – drop valves
Hp: 100	*Rpm:* 28 - 30 *Psi:* 40
Service:	Bank haulage and braking for trucks in transit between pits and River Tyne

This was virtually as built and regularly used in the 1950s until rearrangements made many bank haulages superfluous. The trucks were raised over 760 yards of grade of 1 in 19 at 8 mph, and lowered down the other side. Two drums each 8ft diameter (one for each side of the incline) were fitted, the engine being reversed by slip eccentric to haul up either incline, the engine being placed at the top. The neat boss in the centre of the connecting rod, and ornament on the valve chest cover were typical of the early craftsmen. The use of a stay to the upper floor to take the weight of the eccentric strap was uncommon.

93 Washington, nr Sunderland, Washington Colliery, F Pit — SER 1300

Type:	Horizontal double cylinder
Photo taken:	1967
Maker and Date:	Grange Iron Works, 1888
Cylinder/dimensions:	30in x 4ft 6in – Cornish valves
Hp: ?	*Rpm:* 60 *Psi:* 80
Service:	Coal winding, shaft 960ft deep to Busty seam, drum 10ft? diameter

Washington is a very old coal site, working having started in 1744, with the various shafts lettered up to *J* pit of 1903. There were 9 boilers at *F*, but latterly only 6 were used with the two winding engines and a small auxiliary steam load. Latterly *J* was winding two tons of coal per wind, but had turned three tons per wind when up to 11,000 tons per week was won from the Busty seam. The exhaust steam was used to heat the boiler feed water. All coal working had ceased at Washington by 1973, but the *F* engine has been preserved and is an excellent monument to the later Co. Durham engineers. The governor controlled cut-off action was retained at the Washington pits to the end, but there was no low pressure turbines at *F*; The site there is now an open recreational area.

94 Wheatley Hill, nr Durham, Wheatley Hill Colliery   SER 1299a

Type:	Vertical double cylinder
Photo taken:	1967
Maker and Date:	Dunlop, Meredith, Hartlepool, No 16, 1874
Cylinder/dimensions:	36in x 6ft 0in, as built – Cornish valves
Hp: ?	*Rpm:* 36 *Psi:* 80? Later 140
Service:	Coal winding, shaft 1020ft, drum 17ft 6in diameter

The shafts were sunk in the early 1870s, with a vertical engine on each shaft, using steam at about 80 psi. The colliery ran thus until the mid 1920s, when a major re-organization was effected. Three Babcock water tube boilers were installed, and an Adamson mixed pressure turbine and air compressor, and an alternator, were installed about 1935. The turbo compressor was never fully loaded, and after nationalisation it was replaced by an electrically driven Belliss & Morcom piston type compressor, of half power. The history was confused, as the turbine generator was said to have been abandoned in 1935. In 1929, the No.2. shaft vertical engine was taken out, and a Robey horizontal drop valve double cylinder put in, and the two steam winding engines continued to run the pit until it was closed, about 1968.

95 Wheatley Hill, nr Durham, Wheatley Hill Colliery   SER 1299b

Type:	Horizontal double cylinder
Photo taken:	1967
Maker and Date:	Robey & Co., Lincoln, 1929
Cylinder/dimensions:	32in x 5ft 0in – drop valves
Hp:	*Rpm:* *Psi:*
Service:	Coal winding, shaft 1020ft deep, drum 17ft 6in diameter

This is the new engine (works Nos. 43979 & 70) which replaced the No.2. vertical engine in 1929. It did much coal winding, and was a standard Robey engine. There were three cage decks and certainly three tubs of coal were wound per wind. Latterly the coal was worked from another shaft, and Wheatley Hill, after running for man and material winding, and a compressed air supply unit, was closed in the late 1960s, and all the plant scrapped.

96 Whitburn, nr Sunderland, Whitburn Colliery   SER 1296b

Type:	Double cylinder horizontal.
Photo taken:	1967
Maker and Date:	Walker Bros., Wigan? c. 1890s
Cylinder/dimensions:	33in x 6ft 0in – Corliss drop valves
Hp: ?	*Rpm:* 40 *Psi:* 175
Service:	Coal winding, shaft 1100ft deep, drum 23ft diameter

These were believed to have been made by Walker Bros. when the pit was sunk, but little positive history was known. The original steam pressure was 80 psi, possibly with piston valve cylinders but the boilers were replaced with Babcock water tube units in 1933, and the present cylinders were then fitted by Walker Bros. for 175 psi, the originals probably being 38in or 40in bore. New drums were fitted at some time, together with slow banking and overwind prevention equipment. Always a busy pit, the reserves were not great by the 1960s, and it was intended to work out the coal with the equipment there.

97 Whitburn, nr Sunderland, Whitburn Colliery — SER 1296c

Type:	Horizontal cross compound.
Photo taken:	1967
Maker and Date:	Walker Bros., Wigan, c. 1890s
Cylinder/dimensions:	About 14in and 30in x 4ft 0in – Corliss and slide valves
Hp: 350	*Rpm:* 70 *Psi:* 150
Service:	Mine ventilation, 10 rope drive to pulley for Walker's fan

This was for the original fan, and was fitted with a slide valve engine using the lower initial steam pressure. It was always a compound engine, and when the winding engine (SER 1296b) was changed to use the higher steam pressure, Walker Bros. also fitted a new high pressure cylinder to this. Although this was much smaller than the original one, the Corliss valves still would not clear the bedplate, so the exhaust as well as the inlet valves were placed at the top. The original low pressure slide valve cylinder was retained. With the general adoption of electrical driving at the colliery, the fan and engine were replaced by the motor and drive at the left, retaining the steam fan as a standby for the repair and cleaning period.

Northumberland

98 Ashington, Woodhorn Colliery — SER 1448

Type:	Double cylinder horizontal
Photo taken:	1972
Maker and Date:	Grant, Ritchie, Kilmarnock, c. 1900
Cylinder/dimensions:	28in x 6ft 0in – Cornish valves
Hp: ?	*Rpm:* 35 *Psi:* 100
Service:	Coal winding, shaft 800ft deep, rope drum 16ft diamenter

The No. 1 and 2 shaft engines were identical although No. 2 shaft was less than 400 feet deep, and they were supplied new to the colliery. Neither expansion gear, or piston tail rods were ever fitted. The cylinders may originally have been 30in bore; new cylinders, identical to the originals but smaller, being fitted later. When the plant was all steam driven, the pit being quite independent, there were 14 Lancashire boilers, generally 12 in use, for the two winding engines, capstans, generating and air compressing, and pumps, but by the 1960s there were less than six. A very unusual feature at Woodhorn Colliery was that the dial of the depth indicator revolved, with the pointer fixed. It was the only case I met where the indicating hand was stationary.

99 Mitford, nr Morpeth, Ashton, Jos., Abbey Mill — SER 1018

Type:	Undershot water wheel
Photo taken:	1960
Maker and Date:	Maker unknown,1863?
Cylinder/dimensions:	16ft 0in x 4ft 6in wide
Hp: 8 – 10	*Rpm:* 20 *Psi:* ?
Service:	Blanket making. Local people's wool made into blankets

The mill was run by Mr. J. Ashton until he was 80 years old, and probably his father had done so before. The mill was nearly 100 ft from the water wheel and was driven from it by an underground shaft about 100ft long and 2in diameter. The drive from the waterwheel can be seen in the photograph, a pair of spurgear wheels driving up to the shaft carrying the bevel wheels and the 2in shaft, which can be seen passing to the left, to the underground channel and the mill on the other side of the road. It was a quaint little plant with a complete set of woollen manufacturing machinery, driven by very little power, which had served the local community for a long time but was derelict in 1960. A possible clue to the date was that 1863 was cut into one of the uprights of the mill framing, which may have been the start of woollen milling there.

100 Mitford, nr Morpeth, Brown & Co., Sawmill   SER 1276

Type:	Single cylinder overtype
Photo taken:	1966
Maker and Date:	Wm Foster & Son, Lincoln, No 14724
Cylinder/dimensions:	10 $\frac{1}{2}$ in x 1ft 0in – slide valve
Hp: 20	*Rpm:* 120 *Psi:* 150
Service:	Mill drive by belt from flywheel

This was one of the engines made for the Forestry commission for 1939 wartime service, and sold after the war to a northern mill, was then purchased by Messrs. Brown, who in 1966 had purchased a new saw bench for the Foster engine to drive. These were fitted with colonial type, large engine fireboxes for waste wood firing, and this did very good work and cleared the mill of refuse timber. The flywheels were 4ft 6in diameter, and the boiler 14ft 6in long over all.

101 Newcastle-upon-Tyne, Museum of Science
& Engineering   SER 1460b

Type:	Two beam engines with slide valves
Photo taken:	1973
Service:	Factory drives

These exhibit quite different small early mill engine types. The nearer one is a condensing centre beam engine by Beale of Greenwich of about 1849 – a compact and highly economical form mounted on condenser tank bed. It ran for over a century, mostly at Glemsford Silk Mill, near Sudbury, Suffolk (SER 207) where it assisted the water wheel, and developed up to 40 h.p. The other is smaller and much simpler, being about 15-20 hp, and always non-condensing. No history is known, other than on the label, but it had certainly been heavily loaded, over many years. Seen side by side, they are intriguing contrasts in approach for the small power user, with many differences in design details.

102 Stocksfield, nr Corbridge, J Moffatt, Peepy Farm   SER 1295

Type:	Vertical single cylinder
Photo taken:	1967
Maker and Date:	Gilkes? 1850s
Cylinder/dimensions:	8in x 1ft 6in – slide valve
Hp: 10	*Rpm:* 40 *Psi:* 60
Service:	Barn threshing engine. Preserved in fine private collection of North East farm plant

The late summers and ripening of grain in the North East, and the indifferent weather led to the early use of barn threshing machinery in the Border counties. Small farms used horses for driving the threshing machines which were a part of the barn itself, but the larger farms adopted steam power. They were often locally built and this one was probably made for a large estate, the Gothic features may well match the predominating architecture of the other buildings. Gothic was not a common engine style, and in this case the cast iron curved side members, support-ing the crankshaft bearing overhead, also form the steam and exhaust pipes. Seen partly erected, it is of the Crowther type so widely used for colliery winding in the area, which was probably a source of the prosperity of the estate which it served. It is preserved complete with the barn threshing machine it drove, which is on the other side of the wall.

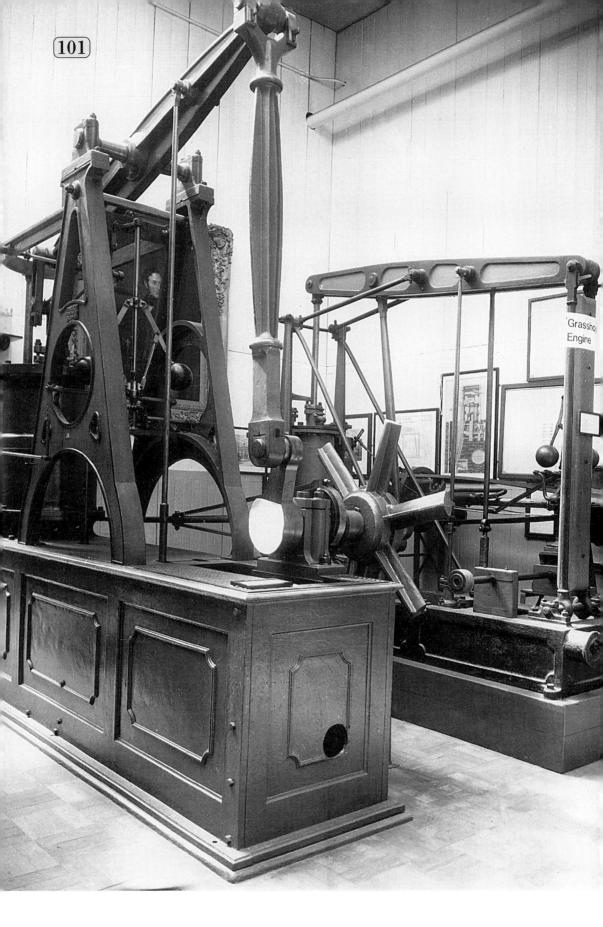

101

Extra photographs from the Contact Print Books

103 *Auckland Park, nr Bishop Auckland,*
Auckland Park Colliery   CPB/SER566

View of top of the engine flywheel and winding drum.

104 *Beamish, Beamish Colliery, Chop Hill Pit*   CPB/SER614

The engine house and pit head. This, with the engine, is restored and is a working exhibit at the Beamish Open-Air museum. In the foreground are the damper controls for the boiler flues, with the lagged boiler tops in the middle right. The pit bank and screens are to the right of the photograph.

105 *Easington, Eppleton Colliery*   CPB/SER3 76

Bottom of winding drum at right, connecting rod and link piece of the Crowther parallel motion to the left.

106 New Herrington, New Herrington Colliery   CPB/SER564

Engine house and pit head. In the foreground are rolled steel joists curved to act as tunnel supports in the mine. Behind them and between the brick engine house and the pithead is the pit bank containing the coal screens, with a shoot for coal trucks above the railway track in the centre. It was customary for the pit bank to be about 20ft above ground level, to allow the coal to pass through the stages of screening by gravity.

107 Sherburn Hill, Sherburn Hill Colliery, East Pit   CPB/SER377b

Cast iron A frame for the wheel supports at the rear. In the front the beam, link piece and connecting rod of the Crowther parallel motion.

108/109 Sunderland, Monkwearmouth Colliery   CPB/SER 369b

George Watkins photographed both of the winding engine drums but it is not possible to identify them separately.

SERIES EDITOR, TONY WOOLRICH

Tony was born in Bristol in 1938. He became interested in technical history in his school days, and has been a Member of the Newcomen Society for 40 years, for ten years of which serving as a sub-editor of the *Newcomen Transactions*. He is also a Member of SHOT (the Society for the History of Technology), ICOHTEC (the International Committee for the History of Technology) and the Somerset Archaeological and Natural History Society.

He trained as a craftsman in the engineering industry, and from 1970 has combined his craft and historical skills in modelmaking for museums and heritage projects.

He has also published books and articles on aspects of technical history and biography. A particular interest is industrial espionage of the 18th century. Another interest is 18th century and early 19th century technical books and encyclopaedias, in particular Rees's *Cyclopædia*, (1802-1819). He has been working on a biography of the engineer John Farey, jr (1791-1851) for the past 20 years.

Since 1989 he has been heavily involved cataloguing for the National Monuments Record, Swindon, the Watkins Collection on the Stationary Steam Engine. He is also a constant consultee to the Monuments Protection Programme of English Heritage.

Since 1994 he has been acting as a contributor to the New *Dictionary of National Biography* working on biographies of engineers and industrialists. He is a contributor to the forthcoming *Biographical Dictionary of Civil Engineers*, published by the Institution of Civil Engineers.

He has recently completed for Wessex Water plc a study of the water supplies of Bridgwater, Wellington (Somerset) and Taunton, and was part of the team setting up the company's education centres at Ashford (near Bridgwater) and Sutton Poyntz (near Weymouth).

 # ENGINE MAKERS INDEX

Maker	SER No.	Plate No.
Unknown	1270a	1
Belliss & Morcom	1270b	2
Musgrave & Son., J	1264	3
Thompson, Son & Co.	1267	4
Grant, Ritchie	1252	5
Kilmarnock Engineering Co.	1253	6
Wood, John	1251	7
Douglas & Grant	1049	8
Grant, Ritchie	1271a	9
Inglis & Co.	1271b	10
Barclay & Co., A	1250	11
Skedd, James	1294	12
Perran Foundry	560	13
Harvey & Co.	561	14
Duncan Stewart	1047a	15
Unknown	1047b	16
Yule, John	1273	17
Yule, John	1273a	18
Turnbull, Grant & Jack	555	19
Wood Bros & Marsden's	1289	20
Fullerton, Hodgart & Barclay	1257	21
Shearer & Pettigrew	1255	22
Unknown	1256	23
Murray & Paterson	1445	24
Gibb, Hogg & Barclay	1254a	25
Inglis & Co.	1254b	26
Unknown	562a	27

Maker	SER No.	Plate No.
Inglis & Co.	562b	28
Grant, Ritchie	1293	29
Grant, Ritchie	1290	30
Aitken & Co.	1291	31
Inglis & Co.	1292a	32
McTaggart & Co.	1292b	33
Carmichael	1262b	35
Pierce Bros	1263b	37
Robey & Co.	1259	38
Douglas & Grant	1268	39
Petrie & Co., J	1046	40
Douglas & Grant	1048	41
Aimers, McLean	1275	42
Petrie & Co., J	1019	43
Douglas & Grant	1258	44
Bailey & Son, W. H.	1443	45
Willans & Robinson	612	46
Perran Foundry	554a	47
Carels Frères	1249	48
Bever, Dorling	1444	49
Davy Brothers	1247	50
Millburn Engineering	1248	51
Murray & Co., T	566	52
Joicey, J & G	614	53
Joicey, J & G	614a	54
Joicey, J & G	615	55
Joicey, J & G	374a	57
Joicey, J & G	515	59
Murray & Co., T	375a	60
Murray & Co., T	375b	61
Murray & Co., T	378	63
Unknown	378	63

ENGINE MAKERS INDEX

Continued...

Maker	SER No.	Plate No.
Barclay & Co., A	567	64
Dunston Engineering Co.	613	65
Davy Bros.	372	66
Teasdale Brothers	513	67
Ruston Hornsby	1496	68
Yates, W & J	1017	69
Murray & Co., T	376a	70
Joicey, J & G	376b	71
Joicey, J & G	376c	72
Unknown	565a	73
Davy Brothers	565a	74
Walker Brothers	568	75
Richardson, T	370a	76
Richardson, T	370b	77
Worth McKenzie	370c	78
Murray & Co., T	564	79
Hawthorn, R & W	371a	80
Hawthorn, R & W	371b	81
Murray	377a	82
Tangye Ltd.	1277a	84
Tangye Ltd.	1277b	85
Murray & Co., T	369a	86
Joicey, J & G	369a	86
Murray & Co., T	369b	87
Bever, Dorling & Co.	563	89
Varley & Yeadon	1298a	90
Barclay & Co., A	1298b	91

Maker	SER No.	Plate No.
Murray & Co., T	373	92
Grange Iron Works	1300	93
Dunlop, Meredith	1299a	94
Robey & Co.	1299b	95
Walker Brothers	1296b	96
Walker Brothers	1296c	97
Grant, Ritchie	1448	98
Foster & Son, Wm	1276	100
Beale	1460b	101
Unknown	1460b	101
Gilkes (?)	1295	102

Maker	CPB SER No.	Plate No.
Murray & Co., T	566	103
Murray & Co., T	377b	107

Waterwheels.

Maker	SER No.	Plate No.
Kerr & Co., J	1262a	34
Thompson Bros.	1263a	36
Unknown	1018	99

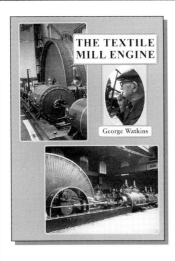

THE TEXTILE MILL ENGINE

By George Watkins

*Produced in the same format, including over
150 plates of engines.*

*Formerly produced as two volumes, these are now published together.
The engines are cross-indexed to both engine types and makers
By and large, these photographs will not appear in
Stationary Steam Engines of Gt Britain*

N.B. Stocks of this book are now limited.

232pp paperback £22.50
ISBN: 1 901522 43 1

Full details upon request

LANDM▲RK
Publishing Ltd ●●●

Waterloo House, 12 Compton, Ashbourne, Derbyshire DE6 1DA England
Tel 01335 347349 Fax 01335 347303
e-mail landmark@clara.net web site: www.landmarkpublishing.co.uk

LANDMARK COLLECTOR'S LIBRARY

LANDMARK COLLECTOR'S LIBRARY

STATIONARY STEAM ENGINES OF GREAT BRITAIN

THE NATIONAL PHOTOGRAPHIC COLLECTION

VOLUME 3: LANCASHIRE PART 1

George Watkins

LANDMARK COLLECTOR'S LIBRARY

LANDMARK COLLECTOR'S LIBRARY

STATIONARY STEAM ENGINES OF GREAT BRITAIN

THE NATIONAL PHOTOGRAPHIC COLLECTION

VOLUME 3: LANCASHIRE PART 2

George Watkins

LANDMARK COLLECTOR'S LIBRARY

Stationary Steam Engines of Great Britain
The National Photographic Collection

THE VOLUMES:

1   Yorkshire

2   Scotland, Cumberland, Co Durham, & Northumberland

3   Lancashire (two books)

4   Wales, Cheshire, Shropshire

5   North Midlands: Derbyshire, Leicestershire, Lincolnshire, Nottinghamshire, Staffordshire

6   South Midlands: Berkshire, Bristol, Buckinghamshire, Gloucestershire, Herefordshire, Hertfordshire, Oxfordshire, Warwickshire, Worcestershire

7   The South and South West: Cornwall, Devon, Dorset, Hampshire, Isle of Wight, Somerset, Wiltshire

8   London & South East: London, Kent, Middlesex, Surrey, Sussex

9   East Anglia: Bedfordshire, Cambridgeshire, Essex, Norfolk, Northants, Suffolk

10 Marine engines

General Specification for all Volumes

Hardback, sewn binding with a laminated dust jacket. Printed on high quailty paper, size: 246 x 172mm (approx 9.75 x 6.75 inches).

Prices will vary according to length. Volume 1 is the longest book. On some of the smaller volumes, opportunity may be possible to incorporate additional photographs from George Watkins' field note books, which are additional to the main engine record and not generally available. Volume 3 (Lancashire) will be split into two parts.

Hardback books on local history which you will enjoy having and dipping into time and again.

Full details upon request

LANDMARK
Publishing Ltd ●●●

Waterloo House, 12 Compton, Ashbourne, Derbyshire DE6 1DA England
Tel 01335 347349 Fax 01335 347303
e-mail landmark@clara.net web site: www.landmarkpublishing.co.uk

PUBLISHER'S NOTE

Corrections

Several readers have kindly contacted us with comments about Volume 1. Some of these comments (and those relating to subsequent volumes) will be published in Volume 10. Others relate to what would appear to be inaccuracies on the publisher's behalf. However, we are producing the collection as it stands. Therefore if two photographs have the same SER number, for instance, that is how it will appear.

We are trying to correct some errors in George Watkins' text – he was frankly not very good at geography and some of the locations of engines could have been better recorded. However it is not our intention to cross-check the accuracy of his extended captions. It would take years to complete even if it was possible to find records to verify his comments and observations.

In Volume 10, we will also include a list of sites for which no photographs were taken but for which there are historical notes of value.

Change of address

From April 2001, please send mail to:

Landmark Publishing Ltd.,
Ashbourne Hall,
Cokayne Avenue,
Ashbourne,
Derbyshire,
DE6 1EJ

Telephone/fax numbers and e-mail will remain unaltered.

Lindsey Porter.
Landmark Publishing.

 # ACKNOWLEDGEMENTS

Thanks are due to Keith Falconer who had the foresight to acquire the collection for the RCHME, and to Helga Lane, (late of the RCHME Salisbury office) who made the original computer database of the Steam Engine Record.

Much help in the production of these volumes has been given by David Birks, National Monuments Record Archives Administration Officer; Anna Eavis, Head of Enquiry and Research Services, and the members of the public search room staff at Swindon.

The often difficult proof-checking was done by Colin Bowden, Brendan Chandler and Jane Woolrich.